C0-AVC-538

GREAT LIVES IN BRIEF

A Series of Biographies

HENRY FORD *by Roger Burlingame*
MAHATMA GANDHI *by Vincent Sheean*
ALEXANDRE DUMAS *by André Maurois*
HANS CHRISTIAN ANDERSEN *by Rumer Godden*
CHARLES DARWIN *by Ruth Moore*
JULIUS CAESAR *by Alfred Duggan*
JAMES J. HILL *by Stewart Holbrook*
ELIZABETH I *by Donald Barr Chidsey*
NAPOLEON III *by Albert Guérard*
GILBERT STUART *by James Thomas Flexner*
NAPOLEON I *by Albert Guérard*
ROBERT E. LEE *by Earl Schenck Miers*
GARIBALDI *by Denis Mack Smith*
WOODROW WILSON *by John A. Garraty*
LOUIS PASTEUR *by Pasteur Vallery-Radot*
ST. FRANCIS OF ASSISI *by E. M. Almedingen*

These are
BORZOI BOOKS
Published by ALFRED A. KNOPF
in New York

LOUIS PASTEUR

TRANSLATED FROM THE FRENCH BY

Alfred Joseph

Louis Pasteur

A GREAT LIFE IN BRIEF

BY

Pasteur Vallery-Radot
Member of the *Académie Française*

New York ALFRED A. KNOPF 1970

L. C. Catalog card number: 58–5828

THIS IS A BORZOI BOOK,
PUBLISHED BY ALFRED A. KNOPF, INC.

PUBLISHED
REPRINTED THREE TIMES
FIFTH PRINTING, SEPTEMBER 1970

FOREWORD

Among the giants of science whose discoveries had a decisive influence on the progress of mankind, Louis Pasteur must be considered as outstanding. He was endowed with those attributes that are the mark of genius, above all bold imagination and exceptional intuition. Whenever he approached a problem, he envisioned the solution and knew which road to follow, without being dependent on preconceived ideas.

Surprisingly, with all his intuition and imagination, Pasteur had an extremely logical mind. Thus each of his discoveries was linked to one that preceded it. From his work in crystallology to that on vaccination, seemingly unrelated, his investigations followed a harmonious plan.

When he had outlined a working program, he used to subject the process to the most rigid experimental tests. As he said: "Imagination should give wings to our thoughts but we always need decisive experimental proof, and when the moment comes to draw conclusions and to interpret the gathered observations, imagination must be checked and dominated by the factual results of the experiment." He could never have achieved his colossal work had he not been possessed by an extraordinary drive. With utmost perseverance he concentrated on his work, his only passion.

Like his scientific prowess, Pasteur's moral fiber was incomparable. When we consider his personal life, his strength of character stands out. Invariably he followed the path outlined by his conscience, and once he had assigned himself a task, he pressed unswervingly to his goal. In his never-ending controversies with opponents whom he was determined to convince, he was not motivated by pride but by his passion for the truth.

These moral qualities could not be impaired by anguish at the loss of his children, nor by the handicap of the partial paralysis that afflicted him after his forty-seventh year, nor by the infamous attacks of jealous people trying to hinder his triumphal progress. His unquenchable spirit gave him "the strength to move mountains," as he once wrote to his wife, who shared his hopes and ideas.

Pasteur's spiritual life was imbued with lofty ideals: sincerity, honesty, decency, and affection for truth. If he is one of the most admired and beloved of geniuses, it is because he stood for everything associated with human greatness: noble character, ever-regenerating enthusiasm, courage and willingness to sacrifice, creative and unselfish work, compassion for suffering, reverence for all that is great and beautiful, love of his country, faith in the value and dignity of man.

We owe to Pasteur the development of a new branch of science: stereochemistry. We owe to him not only the discovery of the nature of fermentation, but also the prosperity of several industries. We owe to him the method of protection from contagious diseases, the principles of vaccination, and measures for controlling epidemics. And finally we owe him a tribute for having dispelled the specter of blood poisoning following surgical operations and childbirth. Thus he has pushed back the frontiers of death; it has been justly stated that Pasteur was one of the great benefactors of mankind.

As the last descendant of this "most perfect man ever to enter the kingdom of science" I have been honored to present the story of his life.

Pasteur Vallery-Radot

LOUIS PASTEUR

I

WHEN the traveler crosses the Jura Mountains on a journey from France into Switzerland, it might occur to him to climb a ridge that takes him to the village of Nozeroy, overlooking the Miège valley. Alongside the fortified walls, vestige of a feudal castle that had welcomed illustrious guests such as Louis XI and Charles the Bold, he will come upon a statue of Pasteur bearing the inscription: "Here the Ancestors of Pasteur Tilled the Soil." Here, in the villages below, these ancestors of Pasteur lived; they were peasants, serfs of the seigneur of that region.

One day, about the year 1760, one of them, Claude-Etienne Pasteur, was attracted to near-by Salins. To him this little town seemed to hold fabulous promise. He had heard stories that in the thirteenth century Jean l'Antique, Lord of Nozeroy, had amassed a huge fortune by exploiting the rich saline fountains he had seized there.

Claude-Etienne Pasteur wanted to be a free man. He gained his freedom on March 20, 1763, by paying 4 gold pieces of 24 livres to the Count of Udressier. He started to work as a tanner's helper and soon owned a small tannery on the outskirts of Salins. Of his ten children one was a boy, Jean-Joseph, born on

May 16, 1791. He was destined to become the father of the genius Louis Pasteur.

After Jean-Joseph lost his parents, he was adopted by his aunts. They put him to work as a tanner's apprentice, to learn the trade of his father and grandfather. He was just twenty years old when he was conscripted into the armed forces of Napoleon. He was assigned to the Third Regiment of the Line, which was campaigning in Spain. It was under orders by the Emperor to round up the bands of Francesco Espoz y Mina, one of the most ferocious among the Spaniards who fought the French invaders.

More than two thirds of the soldiers of the Third Regiment never saw France again. Jean-Joseph Pasteur survived and was promoted to corporal on January 1, 1812, and to quartermaster-sergeant on October 26, 1813. By the end of June 1814 his battalion was recalled to France. It was the moment when Napoleon, assailed from all sides, made a stand against the allied armies in the memorable Campaign of France.

After the battle of Arcis-sur-Aube the battalion in which Jean-Joseph Pasteur served was sent to Saint-Dizier, thence in forced marches to Fontainebleau, which it reached on April 4. There Napoleon was massing his forces for a march on Paris, then threatened by the Allies. The active strength of the battalion had dwindled to 8 officers and 276 men; the rest were dead, wounded, or taken prisoner. On April 5 Napoleon reviewed the Leval division in the courtyard of the Cheval Blanc. From the ranks of the soldiers, devoted to their leader until death, rose the cry: "Long live the Emperor!" In later years this parade was such a touching memory to Jean-Joseph Pasteur that he could not recollect it without tears coming to his eyes.

A few days later the Emperor, abandoned by most of his generals, was forced to abdicate.

The Third Regiment of the Line was sent to the Eure department, and then reorganized in Douai to form a regiment of the King while the fanatic soldiers of the Emperor seethed with anger. Sergeant-major Pasteur was discharged and returned to his tannery in Salins. To him as to every member of the Old Guard the Emperor remained a demigod, and the glory of the victorious years was not dimmed by the final defeat. It had been a beautiful dream, cherished and treasured. The annoyances, vexations, and humiliations imposed by the new regime only served to keep the nostalgia for the past alive.

A stout Bonapartist, Jean-Joseph Pasteur rebelled against the Legitimists, whom he despised, and looked on bitterly as his home town was occupied by the Austrians. The mayor of Salins, ardent Royalist and Knight of Malta, ordered Napoleon's veterans, who were derided as "brigands of the Loire," to surrender their swords at the town hall. Like the others, Jean-Joseph had to submit and grudgingly handed over his saber. But when he learned that these arms, symbols of victory, were to be assigned to police agents, he flew into a rage. He snatched his sword back from the constable, to the applause of the Bonapartists and the indignation of the Legitimists. The mayor asked the Austrian commandant to reprimand the defiant ex-sergeant-major in an exemplary manner. But the colonel refused: "I shall take no action against this sublieutenant of the Emperor; he has been motivated by the military code of honor, which I understand and respect." Jean-Joseph Pasteur kept his saber.

From then on, he led an uneventful existence in his tannery, where he employed a few workers. He was a quiet, pensive man with a slow-working and reflective mind: an introvert with a somber disposition. There was never a smile on his face. He lived inwardly, shut off from his environment, entirely dedicated to his work, which he pursued conscientiously and industriously. On a leather purse that he had made himself and had used when selling hides at the market in Besançon, I found the following inscription in his own hand: "Never think about what one says or does on the spur of the moment."

"You have shown me what patience can achieve by prolonged efforts," said Louis Pasteur of his father, "to you I owe my tenacity in my daily work."

Jean-Joseph Pasteur married a girl from a family of gardeners who lived across from his tannery on the bank of a quiet little river paradoxically named La Furieuse. His bride, Jeanne-Etiennette Roqui, was a modest, inconspicuous woman, interested only in her household. But behind her frigid façade a burning soul was hidden. "My valiant mother, you have passed your enthusiasm on to me," said Louis Pasteur. "If I always have associated the greatness of science with the greatness of my country it is because I was impregnated with the sentiments you inspired."

Shortly after his marriage Jean-Joseph moved to Dôle, where he set up a small tannery along the so-called *canal des tanneurs*. As former capital of Franche-Comté, Dôle had a proud history. In 1034 the territory had passed to the Holy Roman Empire, but its allegiance was generally tenuous, and for six and a half centuries the region was perpetually invaded and contested for by France, Germany, Burgundy, Switzerland, and Spain. It enjoyed relative autonomy under the Spanish crown and was governed by native administrators and by the Parlement at Dôle, composed of representatives of the three classes of the social order: nobility, clergy, and bourgeoisie. The university, founded in 1422, was renowned because of its law school. The heroic resistance of the town against the troops of Louis XI in 1479 has become legendary. "*Comtois, rends-toi!*" cried the attackers. But the defenders refused with a terse: "*Nenni, ma foi!*" words that are now inscribed on the escutcheon of the town.

After Franche-Comté had become a province of the Empire, Charles V had walls erected around Dôle, which made it a fortress of paramount importance. When Richelieu in 1636 decided to occupy the territory, the capital was beleaguered by 20,000 men with 8,000 horses. From trenches dug in a perimeter around the town the attackers launched large grenades that caused tremendous devastation. One assault followed another and all were repulsed. Finally, after three months, the siege was lifted. The archbishop of Besançon, an octogenarian who had been the leading spirit of the defense, had himself carried up to the belfry of Notre Dame (which had served as an observation post) to watch the retreat of the French army. He gave thanks to God and fell dead—his task accomplished.

Several years later, in 1674, Dôle was conquered by the troops of Louis XIV who, to punish the populace for its resistance, razed the ramparts and deprived the town of its charter as a capital. Parlement and university were shifted to Besançon, and Dôle declined.

II

AMIDST the splendor of seventeenth-century palaces in Dôle one will find a very modest house in a narrow, rather gloomy street, surrounded by similar somewhat dilapidated dwellings. There on December 27, 1822, at 5.00 p.m., Louis Pasteur was born.

In 1825 Jean-Joseph Pasteur moved to near-by Marnoz and set up a small tannery. A long time ago I went with my father to visit the site of this old tannery, and to my surprise I found in a cellar, hidden behind barrels, a door with a primitive painting on its panel. It depicts a soldier digging a comrade's grave. The mound holds a cross. The body is half buried, the feet protruding from the pit. The soldier, lost in thought, has interrupted his macabre task and is leaning on his spade. A dog seems to howl. Rugged mountains loom in the background. This panel was painted by Jean-Joseph Pasteur. No doubt he thus intended to commemorate the ill-fated Spanish campaign where so many of his comrades had been slain and buried in haste while the guerillas were harassing the French troops.

When, near the end of his life, Louis Pasteur was asked what his earliest recollection was, he told the following characteristic story: One day when he was with a group of children a stranger, climbing the mountain road to Aiglepierre near Marnoz, promised a shiny sou to the one who would first reach the top. Louis arrived far ahead of his playmates.

At the end of 1827 Jean-Joseph Pasteur bought a tannery in Arbois, a few miles from Marnoz, situated in a plain below the first Jura plateau, on the banks of the river Cuisance. Here he settled down with his wife, his three daughters, and his son Louis. It seems that he had fallen in love with this small town, charming and rich in history. He found himself in a landscape where lovely meadows and vineyards contrast with rocky ridges overhanging the town. The inhabitants are exceedingly fond of their home town and proud of their tradition; they are very hospitable and have a naïve affection for their vineyards, which produce some of France's finest wines.

This is where Louis Pasteur spent his childhood. He often heard the story of Captain Morel of Arbois who, with a handful of men, for three days held in check an army of 25,000. It was under the command of the Marshal of Biron whose orders were to conquer Franche-Comté, which had supported the League against the Huguenots. Despite a pledge given by Henry IV, Morel was hanged from a tree. After their capitulation, the King tried to appease the township by promising to name the wine of Arbois his favorite.

Louis enjoyed listening to tales of the historical glory of the town, and he appreciated the atmosphere of enthusiasm and passion for liberty which pervaded it. In the summer of 1830 unrest spread among the populace of Arbois. They protested against the "July Ordinances" of Charles X, which had suppressed the freedom of the press, dissolved the cabinet, and altered the electoral system in favor of the reactionaries. This provocation sparked an uprising which within four days, from July 26 to July 29, resulted in the overthrow of the Bourbons. The people of Arbois sent a message to the Parisians, declaring that they had been ready to speed to the aid of the capital.

In April 1834 it was learned that Paris and Lyon were again in revolt against the new regime of Louis Philippe. Immediately the good citizens of Arbois seized the guns stored in the town hall, proclaimed the Republic, and were prepared to march on Paris. It took two hundred grenadiers, four squadrons of chasseurs, and half a battery to bring them to their senses. When the subprefect of Poligny asked the insurgents who their leaders were, they replied: "We are all leaders." The next morning, the newspapers carried the memorable phrase: "All quiet in Arbois, Paris, and Lyon."

These experiences helped to forge the character of young Louis. His father sent him to elementary school, then to the high school in town. He was not a child prodigy, and he went by unnoticed. His mind was slow; had he been subjected to the intelligence tests that nowadays are employed to determine the mental alertness of children, he certainly would have been classed as one of the slowest. Jean-Joseph Pasteur, despite his rudimentary education, assumed the role of tutor to his son, who quite often eluded paternal authority to go on fishing trips with his friends. Louis and his companions would follow the Cuisance upstream to the village of Flanches, where the trout to be caught under the rocks were famous.

What he loved even more was to draw portraits in pastel. At the age of thirteen he painted his mother. She wears a white bonnet; her shoulders are draped in a blue-green checkered shawl; her face shows a clear and serene but determined expression. After this first attempt, Louis continued to produce pastels, drawings, and lithographs. Looking at them today one cannot help wondering whether he might not have become a great artist. He sketched deftly, he had a good sense of colors, he knew how to delineate a subject and endeavored to reveal its character. With scrupulous honesty he portrayed his models, not omitting the smallest detail. In this pursuit young Louis gave proof of the conscientious trend that was to permeate his entire scientific work.

Beginning his ninth year in school, Louis came to

appreciate the sacrifice his father had to make for his education, and he redoubled his efforts. His homework records, which some time ago my father and I found in the attic of the house in Arbois, bear out his exceptional diligence. From then on Louis became devoted to his task, and this zeal stayed with him throughout his life. The headmaster of the Arbois college could take credit for recognizing the potentialities of Louis Pasteur. His father nursed the dream that his boy should become a professor at that college, but the headmaster said: "No — one must not steer your son toward the chair of a small college like ours; he ought to be professor in a royal university." Then, turning to Louis: "My young friend, try for the great Ecole Normale." [1]

Father Pasteur hesitated; he did not have such high ambitions. Furthermore, life in Paris would be expensive; the tanner was far from being wealthy; it was not easy to sell the hides that he took to the market in Besançon every month, and he was thrifty like all French artisans. But he knew that there was in the Latin Quarter of Paris, in a street called Impassé des Feuillantines, a pension managed by a

[1] The Ecole Normale Supérieure, founded by Napoleon in 1808, is one of the great French institutions of learning. It prepares talented young men for professorships in science and letters at the universities. The entrance examinations are extremely difficult, and only excellent students are admitted to the contest.

Franche-Comtois, Barbet. He would, as a friend had told him, do for his son what he did for most of his countrymen: lower the rate.

So Jean-Joseph Pasteur gave in, and on a morning in October 1838 young Louis, accompanied by his friend Jules Vercel, left his father's house to commence his year's study of "rhetoric" in Paris. In the coach that carried them away, the two youngsters watched with heavy hearts the familiar steeple of the Arbois church fading in the distance. Hardly arrived in the big city, Louis became homesick. In the Pension Barbet, despite his desire to work, he dreamed day and night of Arbois, of his parents and sisters. It seemed to him that he never would see them again. "Oh, if I only could get a whiff of the old tannery," he said to Jules, "I feel that I would be all right."

M. Barbet, afraid that the youth, who had confided in him, might fall prey to a neurasthenic crisis, advised the father. One morning in November Louis was told, with a mysterious air: "A gentleman is here to see you. He is close by, at the corner of St. Jacques and Feuillantines." The boy raced there. In the back room he caught sight of a figure, seated before a small table, his head between his hands.

"I've come to take you home," the old man said simply. And father and son took the road back to Arbois.

In the months to follow, young Louis Pasteur, a

bit ashamed of his weakness, forced his sensitive soul to submit to discipline. He worked with perseverance at the college of Arbois. At the end of the last school year, when the students enjoyed staging a theatrical performance, Louis was chosen for the role of Alceste in Molière's *Le Misanthrope*. He did so well that for many years people in town commented on his ability as an actor.

III

THE CURRICULUM at the school at Arbois ended with the course in rhetoric. In order to be admitted to the baccalaureat examination the students had to pass a year of "philosophy" at the Royal College of Besançon, about thirty miles from Arbois. Jean-Joseph Pasteur went there every month to sell the products of his tannery at the "Leather Market." The market was held in the courtyard of the Granvelle Palace, a building with an impressive façade, erected in the sixteenth century by an immensely wealthy man who was a councilor in the Parlement and chancellor of Charles V.

Louis Pasteur entered the College of Besançon. He proved to be a good student, appearing reserved, reflective, and withdrawn to his comrades. "I hold a steady place among the best," he wrote to his parents on January 26, 1840. But while he worked diligently, he continued to paint portraits, and reported that he made good progress with colors if not with the likeness. After he had exhibited the picture of a friend in the parlor of the college, everybody wanted his portrait done by the "artist," as Pasteur was nicknamed in town. "All this will not get me into the Ecole Normale," said he. "I'd rather have the first place in college than ten thousand superficial compliments in society."

At the distribution of awards Pasteur received first prize for good conduct and application, the prize for drawing, the second *accessit* [1] in theology, the second *accessit* in Latin dissertation, the fourth *accessit* in physics, the first *accessit* in mathematics. On August 29, 1840, he passed the baccalaureat examination, with the following marks: "good" in Greek (subject: Plutarch) "good" in Latin (subject: Vergil); "good" in rhetoric; "fair" in history and geography; "good" in philosophy and French composition; "excellent" in elementary science.

Now a Bachelor of Letters, Pasteur remembered that the headmaster of Arbois had praised the advantages of an academic career. To this end he had to enter the Ecole Normale; but to be accepted by the scientific department of that school he first had to obtain the degree of Bachelor of Science. He was determined to try his luck.

The Principal of the College in Besançon had singled Pasteur out from among the other students, noting that he loved his work intensely and had the highest sense of responsibility, qualities that would make him "most likely to succeed" in life. At the end of the year 1840, he proposed that Pasteur take on the job

[1] Certificate of merit: In the French scholastic system it is customary to award a small number of *accessits* in addition to the three prizes for the best students.

of a "monitor of supplementary studies," supervising the work of his fellow students while preparing himself for his examination. In addition to room and board he was to receive 25 francs per month. Louis accepted eagerly.

Throughout the years 1840 and 1841 he worked furiously, as shown in his letters to his family. These letters reveal his kind of nature, his love and respect for his father and mother, and his concern about the education of his three sisters: Virginie (born on May 19, 1818), Joséphine (born on March 10, 1825), and Emilie (born on June 14, 1826).

> My dear sisters [he wrote] I beseech you again: work, love one another. Work—at first, I think, it may bring boredom and ennui; but once you have put your mind to it, you'll find that you cannot live without it. Besides, everything in the world depends on it; with knowledge one is happy. . . .

When his parents were reluctant to send his sister Joséphine to a boarding-school because of the expense involved, he wrote them: "Remember that 100 or 200 francs a year do not mean much, and because of such a trifle you might not only spoil Joséphine's education but also her future." He even offered to pay for the upkeep of his sister, the money for which would come from tutoring. During his leisure time he liked to improve his mind by reading the books of a local philosopher, Joseph Droz, who wrote an *Essay on the Art of Happiness* and a *Moral Philosophy,* works now long forgotten. His simple philosophy could be condensed to this formula: Man should strive toward his own perfection; he should have a passion for the good and have the happiness of his fellow men at heart. "The works of Droz," wrote Pasteur to his parents, "convey to me an irresistible charm, penetrating the soul and inspiring the most sublime and generous sentiments." He used to read these treatises on Sundays and became "transported to the most beautiful religious ideas, despite some of it which may be termed inflexible and stupid hypocrisy."

When his parents were worried that he was overworking, he reassured them that he was not working too much and was in perfect health. Throughout his youth, however, he was subject to frequent headaches.

In December 1841 he was the first of his class in physics, and second in mathematics. "If I had gotten such good marks two years ago," he told his parents, "I would have been elated." During the year 1842 he was constantly either first or second; but, like so many young men, he went through a sentimental phase.

Nothing [he complained to his parents on April 30] dries up the heart like the study of mathematics; it dulls the emotions; one sees nothing but geometric figures, letters, symbols, formulas. I who prided myself on my expansive soul, who (during my year of philosophy) prayed to God morning and night with such fervor—now I have given up all this. On Thursday I went out and read a charming story, and I wept. Very strange, for this hasn't happened to me in a long time.

At last, on August 13, 1842, he was admitted to the examination for the baccalaureat in mathematical science. Ironically, the man who was to become one of the greatest chemists of modern times received a mere "mediocre" in chemistry. A few days later, he passed the entrance examinations for the Ecole Normale in the science department. Now he was eligible —but he was dissatisfied with his rating as fourteenth and so he resigned; he was confident of his true worth and he realized what he could accomplish.

IV

PARIS was the traditional fountainhead of learning and the center of intellectual life, and Pasteur realized that he had to return there. In October 1842 he left for Paris with his friend Chappuis, returning to the Pension Barbet. At the sight of it his heart tightened but his days of sentimental schoolboy dreams were over. No more spells of depression—he had to be strong. All that mattered now was to be received with honors at the Ecole Normale and to achieve a career.

M. Barbet allowed him to pay only one third of the usual rate, provided that he instructed the youngsters every morning in elementary mathematics. Soon he was relieved of all expense, in recognition of his exceptional zeal. A touching correspondence went on between Paris and Arbois; the son answered the anxious advice of his father in his simple, forthright, candid manner. When his father, who had to defray the cost of the household and of his daughters' education, once blamed Louis for spending too much money, he answered:

True enough, I have spent too much this year. I know it as well as you and if I could have regulated my expenses better, I wouldn't have to ask you for more money. However, I have never spent large sums at one time; my money dribbled away in 20- and 40-sou amounts; so if I were to give you an expense account it would be difficult for me. I would have to tell you that at one time or other I had to buy paper and pens, then I had a book rebound, I bought a chemistry book by Franklin [probably the translation of Benjamin Franklin's *Memoirs of Physics,* published in Paris, 1773], I took a fiacre because I couldn't find my way when I went to see Mr. Barbier [Officer of the Municipal Guard who regularly spent his furlough in Arbois], I had dinner at the Palais Royal for 32 or 40 sous every Sunday, on Thursdays I went to the theater four times for 45 sous, and once to the Opéra, for four francs. Recently I bought 10 francs' worth of wood, rented a stove for 8 francs, and bought a cloth for my table, to cover the cracks and holes which annoyed me when writing. Three times I had to buy wood when I was with the other students. I could go on talking about these minor expenses, which add up to what I asked you for. Many are one time expenditures, and mainly those for paper, candles, etc. may recur often. Also I ask you only to send me 100 francs in August from now until the end of the year. Then I would have spent this year all in all 600 francs of which you must deduct 60 francs for an overcoat and 60 francs for my room. If that is too much, I don't know how to manage. [And at the end of his letter he added, like a good and respectful son:] Nevertheless, you were right in telling me and blaming me for spending so much; this will make me more economical without curtailing me more than before. And I thank you from the bottom of my heart. However, there was no need for getting so upset, and you don't have to be angry with me.

At the end of the academic year 1843, Pasteur received two *accessits* and first prize in physics at the Saint-Louis Lyceum, where the students of the Pension Barbet took their courses. In the general competition, entered by the outstanding pupils of all secondary schools, he obtained a sixth *accessit* in physics. And in the final examinations for admission to the Ecole Normale he was fourth on the list.

V

IN October 1843 Pasteur entered the Ecole Normale. There was a twelve-hour-a-day schedule. "Everything is well organized" he wrote, full of enthusiasm to acquire as much knowledge as possible. In addition to the courses, there were exercises in chemistry on Tuesdays, supervised by an instructor or the professor himself. Every day for an hour the students could blow glass, and turn out carpentry and locksmith's work, combining theoretical and practical training. To repay M. Barbet for his kindness, Pasteur did not hesitate to put in extra work at the boarding-school, tutoring the pupils.

In early November the Minister of Education paid a visit to the Ecole Normale. Pasteur, like most young men, had a critical mind: he sized the minister up as a politician who indulged in platitudes. "What he said," he exclaimed that evening, "were high-sounding phrases as always, but they meant nothing at all—or very little."

In the correspondence that Jean-Joseph Pasteur kept up with his son, his practical, utilitarian disposition was evident. For instance, he asked Louis to get hold of the lectures on the tanning-process which were given at the school: "This can only be useful to me since everything taught there must be based on experience." As he had known too well the economic hardships of life, he expressed the hope that his son would mainly be interested in mathematics because a professorship in mathematics was more lucrative than one in physics. He added: "I think it's wrong to reject money when it is well earned; it may not bring happiness but it certainly does not prevent it." Continuing in this vein he quoted to his son Napoleon's advice to a modest scientist: "Remember that in this world one must have money, otherwise your merit is diminished in the eyes of the mob."

When Louis worked days and nights, his father, who was temperate in his entire mode of living, became alarmed: "You work immoderately. We are worried about your health. It isn't good to be always high-strung. Ruining your health is not the way to success!" But young Louis was far from accepting his father's view that "You ought to be glad, having arrived at this point. Your ambition ought to be a thousand times fulfilled. Your position is secure when you leave the Ecole Normale. Barely twenty-three years old, you are in line for a post that pays 3,000 francs and is endowed with well-deserved prestige."

Louis Pasteur aspired to a higher goal; he was driven by the desire to advance as far as possible in his calling. It is quite amusing to read, after an interval of more than a century, such remarks in his father's letters as: "Don't go out at night in the bad streets of

Paris!" or the naïve warning, understandable in an era where the machine had not yet taken over: "When you visit a shop where there are machines, don't ever go near the cylinders. Catching the least bit of clothing in them could crush a man."

While giving such advice, the father tried to round out his own education so as to be able to follow his son's studies from afar. He asked for exercises in grammar and arithmetic. The son complied with his wishes; however, to avoid a show of superiority, he added: "I am sending you what you demand so that you can be a teacher to Joséphine."

In September 1846 Pasteur passed the competitive examination for a fellowship in physical science. He was admitted—in third place, because of his poor lecture in natural history. His lecture in physics had been good, the one in chemistry excellent.

"Of all candidates you are the only one who can give a lecture," said his examiner, M. Mason.

"This commendation made me very happy," wrote Pasteur to his friend Chappuis. "We who are called professors should first of all be able to do a good job in teaching." In October he was appointed assistant to the famous chemist Balard at the Ecole Normale, and he attended the courses of Jean-Baptiste Dumas at the Sorbonne.

At that time Dumas was the most celebrated chemist in France. A man of forty-six, member of the Academy of Sciences and professor at the Faculty of Sciences, he had just founded the Central Institute to train the engineers of the future. He gave his lectures dressed in black, with white vest and black cravat; his entire person seemed to exude an official aura. His presentation was clear, facile, but carefully prepared. He did not dwell on details; general ideas and ingenious analogies poured forth in an unending stream, and he conducted his experiments in the overflowing amphitheater with flawless precision.

Pasteur was full of admiration for the great teacher. With the sincerity typical of a superior character he approached the master, coming straight to the point. He wrote to Dumas—to whom he had never been introduced—to ask him whether there might be an opening for an assistant instructor in physics or, better still, in chemistry:

Sir, I wish to tell you in all frankness, which may sound naïve, that it is my ambition to become a distinguished professor. [He went on to say that he intended to devote his life to science; if he were close to Jean-Baptiste Dumas, he could perfect himself in the art of teaching. And he finished with the touching words:] "You will probably excuse my rashness more readily if you recall the time when you yourself aspired to the professorship. I am too young to have seen your beginnings, but surely you have not arrived all of a sudden on the summit;

once you must have prayed for a stepping-stone that would give you a chance to scale the lofty heights where you now reside.

There was indeed no shadow in Pasteur's life; everything was luminous. Subtlety and subterfuges were alien to his nature. He always was true to himself, as in this letter to Dumas. The illustrious chemist could not give Pasteur the position he craved—but he did become interested in the young man who wanted so much to be a noted professor, and who, to further his aims, had made such an unusual and bold advance.

VI

IN August 1847 Pasteur passed his tests in chemistry and physics. He developed an intense interest in crystallology. But then the revolution of 1848 broke out. Paris was in uproar. King Louis Philippe was unpopular; he sided with his Premier, Guizot, who stubbornly refused to make concessions to the people. Duvergier de Hauranne fomented unrest throughout France by political banquets, in which he denounced the regime and demanded reform of the reactionary system of suffrage.

Jean-Joseph Pasteur was concerned about his son's safety. In a letter of February 20, he warned him to stay home and keep away from political activities. Little did he know his son; inflamed by the passion for liberty, Pasteur already was in the midst of the turbulence. When Papa Pasteur's letter arrived at the Ecole Normale, the Republic had been proclaimed and a provisional government had been set up. One of its leading members was the poet Alphonse de Lamartine. In April the government appealed for volunteers to fight the kind of rioters who never fail to appear as the scum of great and idealistic popular movements. Pasteur enlisted in the National Guard.

On April 16, 40,000 demonstrators staged a

march from the Champ de Mars toward the Hôtel de Ville to present petitions. Louis Blanc, who advocated communism, took an active part in this monster demonstration. At 2.00 p.m. the alarm was sounded in all quarters of the capital. Presently streets and squares filled with armed National Guardsmen, "full of spirit," as Pasteur wrote, and "ready to defend the Republic and to restore the respect for order." There were 220,000 of them. Pasteur was at his post at the railroad station of Orléans. In a letter to his parents he said: "Heroic and inspiring actions are performed under our eyes," and he added, "I am getting inured to the din of combat, and if I had to I would fight with the greatest courage for the sacred cause of the Republic."

His father disagreed: "If you feel that you owe something to law and order in Paris, remember that you owe two hundred times more to your family. . . . Whenever there is rioting, stay at home, where you belong." Had the veteran of the Empire forgotten the enthusiasm he had shown to the Emperor? At any rate, his son was of the same mettle. He could not obey the cautious advice of his father; more he was aroused by "the sacred cause of the Republic." One day, when crossing the Place du Panthéon, he saw a crowd gathering around the platform of an improvised barricade. A tricolored banner bore the inscription: "Altar of the Fatherland." Pasteur returned to the Ecole Normale, took out all his savings—250 francs—and eagerly handed the money over to the Republicans.

Pasteur's father could not help being proud of his son's gesture. He asked him to insert in *Le National* or *La Réforme* the notice:

> Gift to the Fatherland, 250 francs, by the son of an old soldier whom the Emperor has decorated.

VII

IN the beginning of May, calm had been restored. Pasteur could resume his study of crystals. Then, on May 21, his mother died suddenly in Arbois. The political tension and worry about her son may well have hastened her end. Pasteur's grief was hardly lessened by the satisfaction with which he had, a few days before, presented at the Academy of Sciences his "Report on the Relationship between the Crystalline Form, the Chemical Composition, and the Direction of Rotatory Polarization." For a long time he had sought the solution to a problem that had baffled the most prominent physicists. Two crystalline substances, the tartrate and the paratartrate [1] of sodium and ammonium, look alike and have the same chemical properties; however, the tartrate turns a polarized beam of light to the right side while the paratartrate is optically inactive. Pasteur wondered why this was so, and wonder is the primary trait of a scientist devoted to the study of nature. To be sure, Pasteur possessed the gift bestowed on superior minds: to perceive what remains hidden from the crowd. Long and

[1] Paratartrate is also called racemate (from *racemus*, grape, indicating the origin of tartrates as by-products in the manufacture of wine, being deposited from the fermented must); racemic is a synonym for paratartaric.

patient scrutiny revealed that the tartrate crystals, which rotated the plane of polarized light, had a tiny facet on one side, overlooked by previous investigators. Pasteur said to himself that if such facets were not to be found on the paratartrate crystals, the difference would be explained. Unfortunately, this was a false hope; close examination of the latter showed similar facets.

Everyone else would have been discouraged. Not so Pasteur; he carried on. He observed that the paratartrate crystals were not all identical, as it seemed; in some the facets were turned to the right, in others to the left. Pasteur painstakingly picked out the "right-handed" and "left-handed" crystals, and prepared solutions of each. He reasoned as follows: the solution of the "right" crystals deviates polarized light to the right, the "left" crystals to the left. Thus a mixture of equal parts of both solutions apparently can have no influence on polarized light; hence the paratartrate, composed of right and left tartrates, was optically inactive.

He made tests with the polarimeter: the result was exactly as he had predicted. Overwhelmed with joy he rushed into the passage of the Ecole Normale, where he embraced a physics instructor with the words: "I have made a great discovery," and dragged him into the Luxembourg Gardens to tell him of his observation.

The report was received with amazement by the Academy of Sciences, then ruled by men like Arago, Biot, Dumas, Senarmont, Balard. They were either astonished or skeptical. To settle the problem they chose Jean-Baptiste Biot, a man of seventy-four who had been Professor of Physics at the Collège de France and Professor of Physical Astronomy at the Faculty of Sciences. As a pioneer in the study of polarized light, he was stupefied by the discovery made by a twenty-five-year-old neophyte, and he found it hard to believe. He summoned Pasteur to his domicile. "Go into the kitchen," he said to him. "Here is paratartaric acid that I have prepared with special care. I have made sure that it is absolutely inactive toward polarized light. Now you will prepare a paratartrate with the sodium and ammonia that we have here."

Louis Pasteur did as told. The solution was left to evaporate slowly. After ten days, Biot asked Pasteur to the Collège de France to examine the specimen. Before Biot's eyes Pasteur picked from the glass jar where crystallization had taken place the "left-" and "right-handed" crystals, placing them to his left and right side. "Well," said Biot, "you claim that the crystals at your left will rotate polarized light to the left, and those at your right will rotate it to the right?"

"Yes," Pasteur simply answered.

"All right, I'll handle the rest," said Biot. He prepared a solution of "levo" and "dextro" crystals in exact proportions and again, some time later, he invited Pasteur to his studio to examine the solutions in polarized light. First he put into the apparatus the solution that was supposed to cause rotation to the left, and with one glance through the eyepiece he noticed a strong deviation to the left. That was all the proof Biot needed; excited, he grabbed Pasteur's arm and exclaimed: "My son, I am so deeply in love with science that this makes my heart beat faster." From this day on, the old master became Pasteur's godfather in his scientific undertakings. Between the two men, one at the sunset of a life filled with glory, the other at the dawn of an illustrious career, a friendship developed which honored both.

His sensational discovery made Pasteur rank among the foremost scientists of Europe. In his subsequent studies, he succeeded in integrating crystallography, chemistry, and optics. This points out how in science extreme specialization can be a mistake; the great laws of nature are uncovered by minds with a broad perspective. Throughout his researches Pasteur exhibited his intuitive genius, his persistent observation of facts, and his exceptional faculty of deduction. He was able to demonstrate a close correlation between the configuration of crystals, their molecular structure, and their effect on polarized light. Thus Pasteur established the fundamental concepts of stereochemistry.

VIII

IN the midst of his studies of crystals, Pasteur was appointed Professor of Physics at the Lyceum of Dijon, on September 16, 1848. Soon he realized that he could not continue his researches there. "Actually, I can't do a thing here," he complained to his friend Chappuis. Fortunately, after three months he was offered the position of Assistant Professor of Chemistry at the Faculty of Sciences in Strasbourg. This university provided at that time liberal resources for instruction and research purposes, owing to the abundant industry of Alsace. Nevertheless, Pasteur longed for Paris: "Ah, where is Paris, with its activities, its inspiration!" he wrote to Chappuis.

Pasteur had hardly arrived at his new destination when he was invited to the house of the Rector, M. Laurent. Immediately he felt attracted to his daughter, Marie. She was a modest, spirited, and cheerful girl, endowed with all the qualities that appealed to the young scientist. But to whom could he confide his affection? To her? Impossible—in those days that would have disclosed poor upbringing, and undoubtedly the young lady would have dismissed him. There was only one way: to turn to her father or mother and, true to convention, ask for their daughter's hand in marriage. Pasteur did not hesitate to write to M. Laurent, on February 10, 1849, a touching letter, giving an account of himself and his family in a simple, sincere, and graceful manner:

Sir: A request of the utmost importance to me and to your family is about to be made on my behalf, and I feel it is my duty to furnish you with this information, which may decide your acceptance or refusal.

My father is a tanner in the small town of Arbois in the Jura. My sisters are with him, and take care of the household and help in the trade. We had the great misfortune to lose our mother last May.

My family is quite comfortable, but by no means wealthy. I would not value our possessions at more than 50,000 francs, and I have long ago decided to hand over my share in full to my sisters. Therefore, I have no property at all. My only assets are good health, an honest heart, and my position at the university.

I graduated from the Ecole Normale two years ago, with a fellowship in physical sciences. I have held a doctor's degree for the past eighteen months, and some studies of mine which I presented to the Academy of Sciences have been very well received; particularly the last one has been found praiseworthy, and I take the liberty to enclose this review.

This, Sir, is my present situation. As to the future, unless my inclinations should change completely, I am determined to devote myself to chemical research. It is my ambition to return to Paris when I have acquired some reputation through my scientific work. M. Biot has often told me that I should seriously think about the

Academy; I may do so in fifteen or twenty years, after assiduous work. Why mention this dream—it surely is not the motive which makes me love science for science's sake.

My father will come to Strasbourg to make a proposal of marriage. Nobody here knows of my intentions, and you may be assured, Sir, that if you refuse me, no one will know of it and your esteem will not be affected in the least.

Laurent hesitated—he hardly knew the young man. He considered him rather impudent. Days and weeks passed by. No answer. Uneasy about the feelings of the young lady, Pasteur on March 31 approached Mme Laurent, in whom he sensed an ally. He was afraid that Marie might have an unfavorable impression of him, for, as he wrote with his usual frankness: "I am well aware that I lack the attributes that instantly attract a young girl. But experience tells me that when people get to know me well enough, they like me." He mustered the courage to write a respectful letter to Mlle Laurent which, however, had to be delivered by the mother—in those days a young man was not permitted to court a girl without the explicit consent of her parents.

An idyllic romance ensued. Marie Laurent—in the presence of her parents, of course—pressed Louis's hand, intimating that she was not indifferent to him. He was deeply moved and could hardly believe in his good fortune. The next day he wrote to her:

My dear Marie, now I am confident that you will love me. Thanks, a thousand thanks for your love. I was so restless . . . I have only one thought: you. My work no longer means anything to me: I who so much loved my crystals, I who used to wish in the evening for a shorter night so that I could sooner be back at my studies.

The outcome was the fulfillment of Pasteur's dream; on May 29, 1849, he and Marie Laurent were married in the Church of Sainte Madeleine in Strasbourg. The story goes that on the morning of the wedding Pasteur was working in the laboratory and had to be reminded of the ceremony. So he had not forgotten his crystals after all!

Marie Pasteur, in her simplicity and kindness, with her good humor, common sense, and clear judgment, and in her constant devotion was the ideal companion for her husband. As Dr. Emile Roux, one of Pasteur's collaborators, wrote: "It looks as if this predestined union had materialized just to help promote the great things Pasteur was to achieve."

After his marriage Pasteur continued his studies of crystals while lecturing in a manner that fascinated his assistants. He inspired the curiosity of his students as well as their enthusiasm, taking a personal interest in every one of them. "I wish," he said one day, "that every lecturer on entering his class asked himself in silent reflection: How can I today raise the minds and hearts of my students to a higher level?"

While preparing his lectures with methodical care, he still devoted five days of the week to his laboratory work. More and more he became impassioned with his research on crystals: "I think I have already told you," he wrote to his friend Chappuis, "that I am on the verge of mysteries, and that the veil which covers them is lifting more and more." This enthusiasm poured forth in the letters he sent to his wife during a journey to Germany and Austria in search of racemic (or paratartaric) acid.

He had learned that a well-known industrialist in Saxony was producing racemic acid, which had been derived accidentally for the first time in 1820 by Kestner in a factory at Thann in Alsace during the manufacture of tartaric acid. But afterward this mysterious acid had suddenly ceased to appear, and Pasteur, anxious to trace its origin, was greatly excited over the possibility of obtaining it. With his inherent impetuosity he immediately made plans to look up the industrialist in Saxony.

"I would go to the end of the world, if necessary," he said. "I must detect the source of racemic acid and find out the origin of the tartrates."

But he did not have the money needed for the trip. He asked Jean-Baptiste Dumas to obtain for him a grant of 1,000 francs from the Minister of Education. Then he started out. On his journey he visited Brussels, Cologne, Hanover ("beautiful town, with a wealthy and noble atmosphere"), Magdeburg, Leipzig ("amidst immense plains where the famous Battle of the Nations was fought"). Finally he arrived at Zwickau on the Mulde where he was to find Herr Fikentscher, the manufacturer who supposedly produced racemic acid. He saw "for the first time immense coal mines, one of which contains one of the biggest steam engines in the world, fetching the water of the mine 900 feet below the surface where 200 men are at work."

The young traveler visited the prosperous factory of Herr Fikentscher, bombarding the owner with questions. The industrialist told him that he had obtained racemic acid for the first time twenty-two years earlier. Then he was able to produce it in abundant quantities. But afterward the yield had diminished to the point that he did not even bother to collect it anymore.

"Have you used the same tartrates for these twenty-two years?" asked Pasteur. "No," answered Fikentscher, "when I obtained racemic acids in quantity, my tartrates came from Trieste." He handed Pasteur two samples of crude tartrates, one shipped from Austria, the other from Trieste. Since there was no laboratory in Zwickau, Pasteur returned to Leipzig, where he requested permission to use the facilities of the university for an analysis of his tartrates.

He wrote to his wife that he was ready to go on to Vienna to study the tartrates from Hungary, and thence to Trieste where he would secure tartrates from the Levant besides the Austrian products. "If I had enough money, I would proceed to Italy, but it is out of the question. That has to wait until next year. I shall pursue this racemic acid even if it takes me ten years, but it will not take that long." A few days later, he resorted to asking his wife to send him money. So that she would not worry about its safekeeping, he added: "My negligence has its limits; I want you to know, and I am proud to say, that between Paris and Leipzig and Zwickau I have not misplaced the least little item."

In Dresden he spent four pleasant hours in the world-famous Museum, checking in a catalog the paintings he liked best. "Those that attracted my attention got a cross, then I made two or three, according to the degree of my enthusiasm; I even went to four." From Dresden he went to Freiberg to meet the Professor of Mineralogy Breithaupt, then to Vienna. And there, in a factory manufacturing tartaric acid he believed he saw on the surface of a barrel "the famous substance." He was not mistaken—this product, which the manufacturer took for potassium sulfate, was no other than racemic acid, in extremely small quantity. Pasteur left for Prague, where he consulted the chief chemist of a tartar factory. This Dr. Rassmann informed him that for a long time he had been obtaining racemic acid by way of tartaric acid.

Pasteur shook his hand affectionately: "Well, if that is true you have made one of the greatest chemical discoveries. Perhaps you don't realize, as I do, the full significance of it. But allow me to say that according to my ideas this discovery seems impossible. . . . I don't ask for your secret—but is it really true? You just take a kilogram of tartaric acid and make racemic acid with it?"

"Yes," replied Rassmann, "but it is still . . ."

"Surrounded with great difficulties."

"Yes."

A few hours later, Pasteur wrote to his wife: "M. Rassmann is mistaken. He never has obtained racemic acid with pure tartaric acid."

He returned to Paris very tired, as he remarked in a letter. A reporter of the newspaper *La Vérité* wrote in his account of this roundabout journey: "Neither treasure nor a fair lady has ever been pursued over hill and dale with greater ardor."

In November 1852, Pasteur was promoted from assistant professor to the position of a full-fledged Professor of Chemistry at the Faculty of Sciences in Strasbourg. Everything went well: success in his vocation, continuous discoveries in his research, happiness in his family life. A daughter, Jeanne, and a son, Jean-Baptiste, were born. Soon a new discovery added to his reputation: he finally succeeded in converting tartaric acid into racemic acid. "There it is," he wrote to his father, "the famous racemic acid (that I went all the way to Vienna to find), synthetically prepared from tartaric acid. For a long time I have considered this transformation impossible. It's a discovery of inestimable consequences."

There is little doubt that Pasteur greatly overestimated the importance of his scientific "Grand Tour" and its implications. However, as we have seen, this journey proved his determination and perseverance and served to disprove false claims by German investigators; eventually, it led to a definite advancement of chemistry.

While Pasteur continued his researches on crystals, he affirmed that there was a definite contrast between the living products of nature and dead matter "in so far as asymmetry is apparently a quality of the molecules which have been composed under the influence of Life. All such substances, whether sugars, starches, albumin, gelatine, fibrin, or cellulose, rotate the plane of polarized light, and in the process of crystallization they assume forms whose mirror-images cannot be superposed on them." He theorized that the principles of Life, which have as their basic characteristic a molecular asymmetry, are generated under the influence of "asymmetric forces." As the chemist in his laboratory could not employ such forces, none of his syntheses was ever asymmetric.

What were these asymmetric forces one had to mobilize? In the middle of the nineteenth century the scientific world was under the spell of the wonders of Nature which men like Arago, Ampère, Oersted, and Faraday had revealed. The action of galvanic currents on the magnetized needle, magnetic fields and terrestrial magnetism, the peculiar flow of magnetic forces, the contrast between positive and negative electricity, these were the problems that intrigued the physicists of this period. To Pasteur's mind all these phenomena seemed to stem from asymmetric actions and movements. For once he indulged in speculations. Thus he exposed crystallizing solutions of minerals to the influence of solenoids and later to that of a powerful magnet (constructed by Ruhmkorff); he had an intricate clockwork made with which he intended, by means of a heliostat and a reflector, to reverse the movement of the sun rays; he wanted to employ a special type of polarized light—and he expected that some day, under such influences, an asymmetric substance would appear. Then he would be at the threshold of Life.

"Louis is too much preoccupied with his experiments," wrote Mme Pasteur to her father-in-law. "Those that he is undertaking this year, if successful, might give us another Newton or Galileo."

Pasteur was less optimistic: "My studies don't go well at all. I am almost afraid that I have failed in all my endeavors this year. Well, let's not give up hope. After all, one has to be something of a fool to undertake what I did." If Pasteur had sublime phantasies, if his was a romantic and passionate soul, he still was a man of reason; he always had the instinct, inherited from his forebears of the Franche-Comté, to keep his feet on the ground. His common sense and logical mind made him relinquish his dream. But his incredibly bold concept stayed anchored in the domain of science and has since been verified: molecular asymmetry and a correlated action on polarized light are attributes of living matter; the chemist in his laboratory has never been able to create an asymmetric substance.

To be sure, synthetic chemistry has made considerable progress since Pasteur's time. Nowadays most natural organic compounds can be manufactured; however, these products are inactive on polarized light, or, to use the scientific term, they are *racemic*. If one wants to change the racemic substance secondarily into one which is optically active, one has to introduce a material that is live or derived from a living organism, such as a mold, a microbe, a ferment, a diastase. This means that Pasteur's concept is essentially correct: asymmetry denotes the great demarcation between organic and inorganic matter.

Pasteur's work in crystallology gave birth to a new branch of science: stereochemistry, which projects the molecular structures in space, not on a plane. Into his researches he concentrated all his devotion and his faith in science, an unconquerable perseverance in search of the truth, and the faculty that makes a genius: to see unlimited ranges beyond the particular phenomenon. All his life he regretted that he did not continue these studies. He was diverted to another route, into the sphere of biology. "Carried away, chained, I might say, by the almost inflexible logic of my investigations," he stated at the end of his life, "I turned from the study of crystals and of molecular chemistry to that of the ferments." We shall see how this came about.

IX

ON September 6, 1854, the Minister of Public Education, Fortoul, offered Pasteur the newly created chair of Chemistry at the Faculty of Sciences in Lille. At the same time he was to be Dean of the University. Pasteur consulted with his master Biot, who advised him to accept. Dean at thirty-two! This almost amounted to a revolution in the French administration, steeped in a tradition which held, quite wrongly, that only mature, or, better yet, old men were suited to fill the highest positions.

Lille was the richest industrial center in the north of France, and a young, energetic man with a dynamic personality was needed to take the helm of the new faculty. The Minister could not have made a better choice. Much had to be done to put the new institute on its feet. There were quarters to be built, laboratories to be equipped, the teaching staff to be organized.

On December 7 the formal installation of the faculty took place. Pasteur proclaimed in his inaugural address that instruction at the Faculty of Sciences would be both theoretical and practical. "The students," he declared, "are welcome to repeat in the laboratory the experiments explained in the lectures they have attended." He enthusiastically emphasized this innovation for the parents of future pupils.

Pasteur devoted himself wholeheartedly to his new functions with a zeal that amazed professors and students alike. His intention was to make the Faculty of Sciences of Lille the leading provincial faculty, and he succeeded. To his duties of dean and professor he added the research work he held so dear, and he displayed remarkable efficiency. This is documented by the comments of the Rector of the university:

> Pasteur is a very distinguished scientist and an outstanding teacher. His instruction is lucid and strictly methodical, his speech animated and agreeable, despite a seeming aloofness. His lectures are admirably prepared, his experiments made with extraordinary skill and complete success. . . . I might add that M. Pasteur has a passion for the science he is teaching; that he, so to speak, buries himself in his laboratory; that he is doing research work which, day by day, contributes to the value of his lectures and to the esteem he enjoys; that he supervises the progress of the students of applied sciences with noteworthy interest; and finally, that he manages the Faculty of Sciences of Lille in a vigorous and intelligent manner which has made this institution one of the finest in the Empire.

A large audience crowded the daily courses in chemistry, physics, and natural history at the faculty. Once a week Pasteur gave a lecture on chemistry as applied to the industrial production of the North, followed immediately by a visit to a factory. There he demonstrated technicalities that could not well be explained on the blackboard.

One day in the autumn of 1856 an industrialist, Bigo by name, asked Pasteur to examine in his brewery the vats in which beetroot juice was subjected to fermentation into alcohol, one of the important sources of revenue in the Northern departments. Bigo was having trouble with his distillation, and Pasteur willingly agreed to help him. All he had at his disposal was a coke-burning stove and a small microscope with low magnifying power. Even so he went to inspect the vats in M. Bigo's cellars. In the fermenting juice of the beetroots he observed uniform micro-organisms in the shape of globules, growing and multiplying. These micro-organisms, and nothing else, he said to himself, must be at the origin of the fermentation, that mysterious process which occurs everywhere in nature—above the earth and beneath it. All the fancy theories propounded to explain this peculiar biological phenomenon—action on contact, catalytic force, concussion of the molecules in the fermenting matter—all that renowned chemists from Berzelius to Liebig had suggested had to be wrong, thought Pasteur. These tiny cells, which, as he observed, reproduced rapidly by sprouting buds, explained the phenomenon of fermentation.

Ancient man had used the powers of those micro-organisms without even knowing they existed. He made bread, brewed drinks, made cheese out of milk —all through the process called fermentation. Leeuwenhoek was able to describe the structure of yeast, but he did not recognize it as a living organism. This honor went to the physicist Cagniard de la Tour (1837), who also expressed the opinion that they probably were at the origin of fermentation. However, this view was rebuked by the masters of chemistry, particularly Justus von Liebig, who were only interested in the chemical changes occurring as end products of fermentation; they were unwilling to accept a vitalistic interpretation. Never mind, they argued, what the microscope shows—that is only an after-phenomenon, not the cause of the fermentation itself.

After observing the micro-organism that brings about fermentation, Pasteur detected in cases of faulty fermentation another, smaller microbe in the form of rods. These were the cause of the so-called lactic-acid fermentation of milk. Pasteur's report on his findings is remarkable indeed. These few pages contain his entire experimental technique, which served to illuminate not only the mystery of the fermentation, but, later on, that of the infectious diseases as well. "One cannot," he declared, "study a fermentative process unless one has a pure culture of the ferment," obtained by breeding in proper culture media. Then this material must be proven capable of reproducing fermentation at will. Thus his microbiological method was established, and he adhered to it consistently for the next three decades.

From then on he was absorbed in the study of the fermentations and of their living agents, and his new investigations, coupled with previous observations, confirmed an experiment he started at the end of August 1857. He caused fermentation of ammonium paratartrate (it is well to remember that this salt is inactive toward polarized light, and that it consists of two tartrates, the levo- and dextro-tartrate, both optically inactive). Under the influence of fermentation, due to the action of a mold, a surprising change took place: in the fermented liquid only levo-tartrate was found. In other words, from a substance that was inactive toward polarized light, he had obtained an optically active substance. There was the proof that a vitalistic process was involved in the fermentation, because only substances derived from live matter are capable of deviating the plane of polarized light. Pasteur's report on the fermentation of paratartrate presented the closest link between his work on crystalline structure and that on fermentation.

X

IN October 1857 Pasteur was appointed Administrator of the Ecole Normale and Director of the Scientific Department of the school. Regretfully he left the Faculty of Sciences in Lille of which he had made a model institution in a period of two years. After his arrival in Paris, he had to look for a place to set up a laboratory. All that was available at the Ecole Normale were two vacant rooms in one of the attics, dark and unsuitable. There was not even a helper to clean the glassware. In summer the heat forced Pasteur to interrupt his experiments. He wrote to his friend Chappuis on June 16:

I would like to follow up these observations, if a temperature of 36 degrees C. (97 F.) did not keep me away from my laboratory, or rather from my hole-in-the-wall. Pity that the longest days of the year are lost for my work [He added courageously:] Nevertheless I am growing accustomed to my garret and would hate to leave it. I hope to enlarge it during the next vacation. You, too, are struggling against the material difficulties of your work. May it rather stimulate than dismay us. Then our discoveries will have even more merit.

A year later Pasteur arranged to have his laboratory transferred to five narrow rooms in a pavilion reserved for the architect of the school. Space there was at a premium so that he had to install his incubator oven in the well of the staircase; whoever entered had to go down on his knees. As his collaborator, the chemist Emile Duclaux, put it: "From this wretched garret, which nowadays would hardly be considered fit as a rabbit's cage, radiated the movement that has revolutionized all aspects of science."

Funds were needed to support the laboratory. Where was he to find them? On December 13, 1859, Pasteur wrote to the Minister of Public Education: "I have absolutely no means to meet the everyday expenses of my research work. . . . I had to contribute the sum of 600 francs of my own money to the cost of the laboratory." Actually, he was for years faced with the problem of how to raise the necessary funds, however modest, for continuing his experiments. The monetary awards bestowed on him by the Academy of Sciences were used for buying instruments and glassware. Sometimes he was full of anxiety, as when he wrote to the Minister again on August 26, 1860:

Since Your Excellency has entrusted me with the honorable position I am holding at the Ecole Normale, my laboratory has subsisted on handouts, one year supported by the Academy of Sciences, another year by compensations accorded by Your Excellency. Several times I had to fall back on my own resources. For instance, during the current year I have sacrificed, and I still do, for my laboratory the money of the Grand Prix in Physiology which the Academy of Sciences granted me last February. . . . In the life of every man who devotes himself to the practice of experimental sciences there is an age where the value of time is incalculable; that is the active age where the inventive spirit flourishes, where every year should be marked by a new advance. Would it be insolent to add that I consider myself to be in this phase of life, and to beseech Your Excellency not to leave me to the pressure of unfortunate obstacles which, as you might be aware, result from the fact that there exist no adequate funds to promote the progress of science in our country.

In our day, looking at the magnificent installations and the almost unlimited facilities available for basic research, one should remember the miserable laboratory of Pasteur from which emerged discoveries that have transformed the modern world.

On June 27, 1859, Pasteur presented at the Academy of Sciences a paper on alcoholic fermentation. He first had submitted it to Jean-Baptiste Dumas and to Jean-Baptiste Biot, whom he regarded as his masters. While he was sure of his superiority when dealing with ignorant or jealous opponents who attacked his work groundlessly, and let them feel it bitterly at times, he remained modest and humble toward men who had preceded him in scientific pursuits and had shown the true qualities of a researcher: scientific integrity, a passion for truth, objectivity in observation and experimentation, and accuracy of deduction.

When he asked Dumas to present his paper he reminded him to dwell, if he deemed it advisable, on the salient facts: the demonstration of the biochemical principles of the fermentation process, and the proof for the first time of the presence of glycerin and succinic acid in large proportion in all wines. He concluded his letter with a comment on what was his constant worry, the penury of his laboratory: "I have to let you in on my misery. You know my situation. As I have only administrative functions, there is not the slightest allotment provided for my laboratory. Just for the initial equipment I spent the funds granted to me by the Academy about sixteen months ago on your request, and more."

While his mind was constantly occupied with researches on fermentation, Pasteur did not neglect his family life. Mme Pasteur, respecting the work of her husband and realizing the importance of his investigations, was not only a perfect wife but also an exceptional collaborator. In her Pasteur confided his hopes, to her he dictated his reports for the Academy of Sciences, and she shared the vicissitudes of his life as a scientist. She had borne him three children: Jeanne (April 2, 1850), Jean-Baptiste (November 8,

1851), Cécile (October 1, 1853). Another girl, Marie-Louise (who later married René Vallery-Radot), was born on July 19, 1858. Finally, in July 1863, Camille was born, but she lived no longer than two years.

In September 1859 Pasteur's daughter Jeanne died in Arbois of typhoid fever. It was a heart-rending experience to the father. In a letter full of tenderness he wrote to his wife:

I wish that after my return there should be between us and with us nothing but our love, our children, their education and their future, together with my dreams as a scientist. For you and for them a life enriched by my work, the success of new discoveries, and warmest emotions. Oh! how would I regret to die without having given you all that!

XI

DURING the years 1860 to 1862 Pasteur was engaged in studies of spontaneous generation. He had just demonstrated that whenever fermentation takes place, whether lactic acid, alcohol, or tartrates are concerned, a living germ could be observed, a micro-organism that developed and multiplied. This microbe was established as the cause of the fermentative process, and every fermentation was linked to a specific ferment.

But whence did these mysterious micro-organisms come? Did they form spontaneously in the fermentable media or did they arise from other, similar "parent" germs? Thus the entire question of spontaneous generation posed itself, a question that seemed to defy a solution.

The problem of whether life can exist without previous generation was more than two thousand years old. Aristotle had stated that "every dry body which becomes moist and every humid body which dries up breeds life." Vergil had maintained that bees originate from the putrefying entrails of a young bull. At the time of Louis XIV similar absurd notions were held by the most learned men. The famed alchemist Van Helmont (1577–1644) wrote that "the emanations rising from the bottom of marshes bring forth frogs, snails, leeches, herbs, and a good many other things." He even went so far as to contend that if one desired to obtain a potful of mice all one had to do was to cork a vessel containing some corn with a dirty shirt, and the grains, exposed to the vapor, would become transformed into sprightly young mice within twenty-one days.

The Italian naturalist Francesco Redi (1626–98) made better sense when he affirmed that the worms seen on rotten meat did not breed spontaneously but were maggots hatching from the eggs of flies. To prevent their appearance, one only had to cover the meat with gauze before exposure; since no flies could alight on the protected meat, no maggots were seen.

At the end of the seventeenth century the introduction of the microscope into science by the Dutch biologist Leeuwenhoek gave the partisans of spontaneous generation new support for their theory; these myriads of living microscopic elements cannot, they claimed, be explained in any other way than by spontaneous generation. Count Buffon, the famous eighteenth-century French naturalist and author, upheld this doctrine.

Then, in 1745 two abbés, Needham and Spallanzani, became locked in a violent conflict. In that year, Needham published in London a treatise in which he backed up the existence of spontaneous generation. This Irish priest hit upon the idea of heating flasks containing organic infusions and sealed airtight, by burying them beneath hot cinders. Despite the heating process which, in the opinion of Needham, should kill off all live germs, the liquids in these vessels became turbid and showed tiny organisms ("animalculae") under the microscope. So there had been spontaneous generation after all!

Abbé Spallanzani in Italy chose to dissent. He let his organic mixtures and solutions simmer for three quarters of an hour to a full hour—and no turbidity occurred, no germs developed. If Needham had seen life spring up spontaneously, argued Spallanzani, it was because he had not heated his flasks to the proper temperature. But Needham did not admit defeat. Spallanzani, he protested, had "tortured his organic infusions, enfeebling or even annihilating their Vegetative Force, moreover he had corrupted the air in the vials by the ardor of the fire," so that formation of living creatures was rendered impossible. The controversy between the two militant priests lasted until 1777, kept alive by experiments, observations, and speculations on the part of naturalists and by religious and philosophical minds.

Pasteur launched his researches on spontaneous generation because he felt that this problem had to be solved once and for all. "At the point where I found myself in my studies on fermentation," he wrote, "I had to form a definite opinion on the question of spontaneous generation. . . . Consequently, these investigations are an inevitable sidepath of my studies on the fermentations."

Dumas and Biot wanted to dissuade Pasteur from such pursuits. "You will not get anywhere," said Biot. And when Pasteur tried to convince him that in the line of his work he had no choice but to tackle this problem, Biot burst out: "This project is a presumptuous adventure, I might even say it's folly." Jean-Baptiste Dumas, when consulted, cautioned him: "I would not advise anybody to dwell too long on such a subject." Only Senarmont came to the aid of Pasteur. "Let him carry on," he said to Biot. "If he finds nothing on the road he is traveling, don't worry, he will not stay on it. But I would be surprised indeed if he does not find something."

Pasteur approached the problem without bias, as he did every scientific study. He solely relied on the experimental method for guidance and control. In his forthcoming enterprise he had to deal with a formidable adversary, Pouchet, Director of the Museum of Natural History in Rouen. This man, a protagonist of the theory of spontaneous generation, had a mentality quite different from Pasteur's. "As it became evident to me by meditation," he wrote in his *Treatise on Heterogenesis,* "that spontaneous generation is another of the methods which Nature employs for the reproduction of her creatures, I applied myself to discover by what procedure one could demonstrate these phenomena." While Pasteur had no preconceived idea and simply expected from the experiment the answer to a given problem, Pouchet wanted the experiment to confirm what he already believed "by meditation." Thus Pouchet violated the basic rule of a scientific experiment, which is that the gravest error lies in the desire to confirm what one believes; indeed one must always experiment without prejudging the outcome. As Bossuet said: "It is the worst aberration of the mind to believe things because one wishes them to be so." This is a maxim Pasteur liked to quote.

What polemics and controversies to establish definitely the doctrine of the non-spontaneity of germs! Pasteur devised the most ingenious experiments, revealing the remarkable fertility of his imagination, his prowess as an experimenter, and at the same time displaying his forceful argumentation. He defied his adversaries, challenged the views of his peers, overwhelmed his opponents with experiments leaving no loophole for criticism. He smashed their objections one after another, and pursued them into their last strongholds. He demonstrated that the air contains micro-organisms, always ready to develop and multiply, and that the most perishable liquids remain unchanged if, after being heated to the boiling-point, they are kept protected from air.

Pouchet and the partisans of spontaneous generation remonstrated: "On heating the liquids that you employ you destroy the very elements that are prerequisites of life."

Pasteur countered this objection with the following ingenious test. He filled a special glass bulb with a sugar solution to which yeast was added. The neck

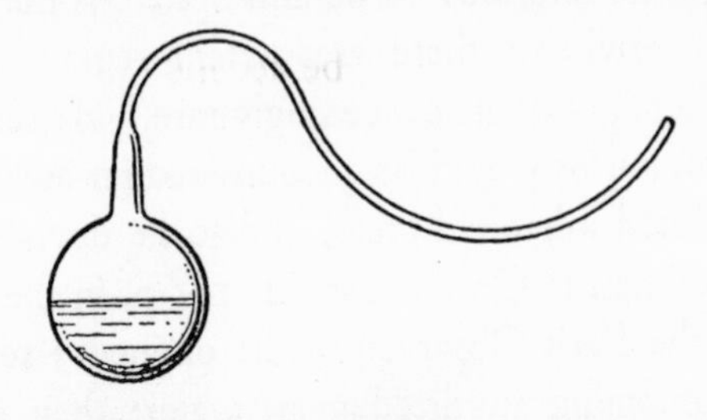

of the flask was drawn out and bent in the shape of a swan's neck; the end was left open so as to permit access of air from the outside. He then heated the bulb to the boiling-point and kept it simmering for several minutes. The fluid, though in contact with ordinary air, remained unchanged for months because germ-laden particles were trapped on the first few inches of the bend. He then turned the bulb so that a drop of liquid touched the dust particles at the end of the neck. Now when the flask was restored to its normal position, it was found that micro-organisms developed in the fluid. Pasteur repeated this experiment several times with the same result. Was not this conclusive proof that the liquid did not lose its properties through heating, and that it could be fecund, provided that germs carried in the dust of the air were introduced?

But the proponents of spontaneous generation hurled another argument at Pasteur: "If your conception were true, normal air would be clogged with organic matter which would form a dense fog."

To this he retorted: "The atmosphere is not germ-laden everywhere; there are certain regions of the globe where germs are exceedingly rare." He reasoned that fewer germs would be encountered far away from dust-polluted inhabited areas, and so he devised control experiments: On August 14, 1860, in the courtyard of the Paris Observatory, he opened a series of bulbs containing sterilized yeast water; they all became clouded after a while. In September he opened 20 flasks in the country, at the foot of the first Jura plateau, far from populated places; 8 became contaminated. He opened another 20 bulbs still farther away, on Mont Poupet at 2,760 feet elevation; 5 became altered.

He did not hesitate to climb the Mont Blanc massif, 6,500 feet high. This expedition was associated with a characteristic anecdote. When he reached the Mer-de-Glace (a glacier near Montanvert), Pasteur opened his bulbs. But when he tried to seal them with an alcohol burner, he was blinded by the glare of the sun reflected from the glacier, unable to see the flame flickering in the wind. By shielding the lamp with his clothes he certainly would have managed to direct the flame to the fine opening long enough to seal it, but then he would have taken the chance of contaminating the mountain air with dust, the very thing he wanted to avoid. So he resigned himself to stay overnight at the miserable little inn at Montanvert, and to resume his experiment the next day before sunrise, with another series of 20 bulbs.

When these were reopened, all except one were found to be sterile. From these tests Pasteur could draw the following conclusions: germs are not evenly distributed in the atmosphere; certain regions are almost germ-free. Therefore, the dust of the air, laden with microbes, is the sole source of life in alterable culture media.

Now Pouchet with his assistants Joly and Musset hastened to the glacier of La Maladetta (10,580 ft.) in the Pyrenees to imitate the experiments made by Pasteur on the Mer-de-Glace. He used an infusion of hay, heated to 100 degrees C. (212 F.)— and his results were in contrast to those of Pasteur.

The dispute between Pouchet and Pasteur did not halt at the portals of the Academy of Sciences. The press got into the fracas. Scholars, writers, philosophers, clergymen, all voiced their opinions, the majority in favor of Pouchet. Never had a scientific controversy aroused so much public interest. At the

Sorbonne on April 7, 1864, Pasteur held a symposium on spontaneous generation before a large audience that included such noted personages as Alexandre Dumas père, Duruy, George Sand, and the Princess Matilde. After having presented his experiments with intense clarity, he rightly concluded: "No—there is today no circumstance known in which it can be confirmed that microscopic beings have come into the world without germs, without parents similar to them. Those who maintain this view are the victims of illusions, of ill-conducted experiments, blighted with errors that they have either been unable to perceive or unable to avoid."

To end the debate, Pasteur proposed that the Academy of Sciences elect a commission before which he as well as the protagonists of spontaneous generation were to present the fundamental experiments "on which they based their contradictory conclusions." While this body was in session, quite a number of incidents occurred, instigated by Pouchet, Joly, and Musset, who tried to find fault with and to sabotage the plans for proposed experiments. Pouchet's agitation reached its climax. "Let's follow Voltaire's maxim," he wrote to Joly, "*écrasons l' infâme!*" The infamous one was—Pasteur.

At last Pouchet, Joly, and Musset withdrew. The Commission finished its work without their concurrence and concluded: "The observations made by

M. Pasteur and contested by M. Pouchet are of the most perfect exactitude." The Commission was then adjourned until the following spring, to comply with a request by Pouchet who, for some reason of his own, considered this season most auspicious for his experiments.

If they had materialized, it would have been quite embarrassing for Pasteur. Actually, while the yeast water he used remained sterile after heating, the decoction of hay employed by Pouchet became populated with germs, despite boiling. On the other hand, Pasteur certainly would have found the solution. However, it was not until fourteen years later that Pasteur, when reminded of this observation by Dr. Bastian during a debate on spontaneous generation, explained the mystery: the infusion of hay contains spores that are resistant to heating; as long as the glass bulb is devoid of air, they remain inert, but as soon as air enters, they develop. To destroy these spores temperatures over 100 degrees C. (212 F.) are required; then the decoction remains sterile indefinitely. Thus Pouchet's deduction was incorrect; the growth in his hay infusions was not the result of spontaneous generation. The necessity of heating liquids and glassware above 100 degrees C. later inspired Pasteur to design the autoclave and the oven named after him.

The discussions between Pasteur and Pouchet, famous in the history of science, were only a prelude to the controversy on the germ theory of infectious diseases.

One should not lose sight of the fact that Pasteur, though he demonstrated that spontaneous generation never occurs in a culture medium, did not consider it altogether impossible, and he often expressed this view. As we have seen before, he himself had dreams about creating or modifying life; thus he sought, by means of asymmetric forces, to break down the barrier that separates mineral matter from the organic products of nature. Who knows what he might have accomplished, had he been equipped with the tremendous technological facilities of our times. In fact, only recently the ancient argument for the spontaneous generation of life has been revived, on the basis of laboratory experiments. These revealed that the basic elements making up living matter can be synthesized out of simple chemicals, under conditions existing on this planet a billion years ago. When methane, ammonia, water, and hydrogen in a closed system were subjected to artificial lightning, nine amino acids were produced, four of which are essential to creating protein, the essence of life.

XII

IN the course of Pasteur's researches on fermentation and spontaneous generation this question arose: How does fermentation work? In other words, how do living ferments act to transform the fermentable matter? The study of butyric-acid fermentation provided Pasteur with the answer. He noted that the micro-organism that caused this fermentation has the property of growing in the absence of air!

This was such a revolutionary biological discovery that Pasteur hardly dared to announce his observation. The great Lavoisier had proclaimed that life was impossible without the oxygen of the air—and now he, Pasteur, asserted that certain organisms can live in the absence of free oxygen! He decided to invite Jean-Baptiste Dumas to his laboratory, together with his fellow scientists Claude Bernard and Balard, to attest the validity of his findings. "In the event that the tests which I repeat before your eyes are absolutely satisfactory," he said to Dumas, "I shall ask you to present my results to the Academy."

So Pasteur demonstrated his experiments to the three experts. They were almost convinced, but then they raised an objection: Suppose the tube in which the butyric ferments were present contained traces of oxygen, sufficient for their life?

Pasteur replied: "If the oxygen of the air kills the butyric-acid organisms, that would be the counter-proof." The test was made: indeed, the oxygen of the air killed the butyric ferments. "Now I believe," said Pasteur to Dumas, "that my conclusions are unassailable. The butyric ferment does not need oxygen to live; on the contrary, the oxygen of the air destroys it. The ferment borrows the oxygen it needs to live from the organic medium and thus decomposes it."

Pasteur suggested the terms "aerobia" and "anaerobia" for the two kinds of life encountered among lower organisms—one which requires the presence of oxygen, the other which exists in its absence. With his ability to proceed from isolated facts to general biological principles, Pasteur advanced the hypothesis that fermentations are a consequence of life without air; that they are due to anaerobic micro-organisms that consume the oxygen of the fermentable environment, causing slow and progressive decomposition.

On December 8, 1862, Pasteur had been elected a Member of the Academy of Sciences, in the Section of Mineralogy. It was the third time he had solicited the votes of the academicians; twice he had suffered defeat, in 1857 and 1861. His first failure had wounded him deeply. Before the voting he wrote to his wife:

I am more and more convinced of my nonsuccess . . . but I am going to work with rage in my heart. I'll be happy when I shall deliver a memorandum with this cry in my soul: You fools! Try to do as well!

His final election was by no means a triumph: he received 36 out of 60 votes. Before the balloting, instead of accepting calmly the objections to his work in crystallology, voiced by the German scientist Rammelsburg and eagerly repeated by his hostile colleagues, Pasteur reacted with a vehemence that shocked the gray-haired, placid scholars of the quai Conti. He insisted that the Philomatic Society devote one meeting to a discussion on crystals, and he contrived to fashion with a plane and saw wooden images of giant crystals, painting their edges and surfaces in different colors. Armed with these forms he went to the Philomatic Society, shaking with excitement. After proving his views, he turned to his opponents: "If you understood the point, where is your conscience? And if you didn't understand, why should you concern yourselves?"

One can imagine the effect of these words. His disciple Duclaux said, referring to this meeting: "M. Pasteur has since won a good many rhetoric victories. I don't know of any more deserved than that achieved by this poignant and brilliant improvisation. He was still fuming when we walked back to the rue d'Ulm, and I remember his laughter when I asked him why he had not, excited as he was, concluded his speech by hurling his wooden models at his opponents' heads."

XIII

THE RANGE of research stretched wider and wider before Pasteur. In an interview granted him by Napoleon III on March 21, 1863, he explained that the investigations he planned "encompassed all the forces of death. Into his tiniest creatures God has placed extraordinary properties that turn them into agents of destruction of dead matter." He assured the Emperor that he was ready to embark on researches concerning the infectious diseases, well aware that he "would need days with more than twenty-four hours to explore this real but hidden treasure."

In April 1863 Pasteur presented to the Academy of Sciences a treatise of major importance, entitled "Examination of the Role Attributed to the Oxygen of the Atmosphere in the Destruction of Animal and Vegetable Matter after Death." Therein he dealt with the mechanism of the cycle of life and death on the face of the earth. What became of animals and plants after their death? How did the destruction of organic matter come about, a process essential to the continuity of life on this planet? How could one explain the perpetual return to the air and to the mineral world of elements which animals and plants have absorbed from them?

Pasteur proved that when organic matter becomes decomposed, aerobic micro-organisms on the surface cause oxidation or combustion, while inside anaerobic germs produce putrefaction. Thus "life presides at the labor of death," death itself being a manifestation of life. "The principal elements of living beings would be virtually indestructible if one were to eliminate from the profusion of God's creatures the smallest and apparently most useless. But, then, life would become impossible if the return of all that has ceased to live to the air and to the mineral kingdom were suddenly suspended."

Marvelous vistas of unknown realms unfolded before Pasteur. One can understand his exaltation and his drive to further explorations. He was fortunate enough to have a companion at his side who appreciated the great mission of her husband and shared the enthusiasm of his dreams. In her affection and solicitude Mme Pasteur consecrated everything to him. She was constantly near him, watching his health and his rest; she tried to spare him every little hardship of life, and reveled in his scientific achievements.

XIV

IN November 1863 Pasteur accepted a chair that had just been created at the School of Fine Arts. It was a professorship directed to the application of geology, physics, and chemistry to the arts. Since his assignment to his duties at the Ecole Normale, Pasteur had not been teaching, and this was heartbreaking to him; he loved teaching almost as much as research. Now he could lecture again, while continuing to manage the Ecole Normale and direct its scientific courses. And though he had not touched a pencil or crayon for twenty years—he had more important things to do—he had not lost his flair for the fine arts.

He delivered his first lecture at the Art School on February 15, 1864. And how carefully it was prepared! Besides having read a number of books on the techniques of painting since the Middle Ages, he had spent long hours in the Louvre and had gathered information from a restorer and from a canvas-maker. He even had gone so far as to have the painter Leloir do before his eyes a portrait of his daughter Cécile so that he could follow all stages of applying the pigments. As always, he displayed the conscientious manner that was ingrained in his character.

During the first year he explained to the students

of architecture the problems of ventilation in dwellings. In the second, he addressed the painters: "The chemist and the physicist will sit down with you and enlighten you." And he explained how the use of a certain pigment, oil, or varnish could affect the durability of a picture. "I don't pretend that I can teach you to make lasting paintings," he said, "but I shall try. I want to call your attention to this problem, and out of our concerted effort perhaps light will come." The man of letters, the artist, and the scientist spoke to the students in these lectures.

He recommended experimental methods, suggesting chemical analysis of pictures by Van Eyck and other Old Masters to find out about their techniques. What good were endless discussions as to whether these masters used varnish, or what the composition of their coating material was? Theories were of no avail here—one had to approach these problems in a scientific way, by examining old pictures chemically. There was also the question of a superior drying agent; to find the answer it would be necessary to test different pigments in combination with the siccatives employed and to observe the time of drying. "Here you see three canvases," he told his pupils, "on which I have applied twenty-three colors of the palette with a certain siccative. With many of these the drying process is long and difficult. Nothing is more annoying to the painter. Now compare and judge for yourself."

It certainly was regrettable that his research work forced Pasteur to give up his courses, for he would undoubtedly have given the students at the School of Fine Arts a wealth of useful instruction in the technique of painting.

XV

PASTEUR was a man with a practical mind. He carried his discoveries from the laboratory into the industrial domain. "Pure science, on its highest level," said he, "cannot advance one step without sooner or later bringing profit to industry from the application of its precious results." Consequently, he discarded a differentiation between theoretical and applied sciences.

No, a thousand times no, [he wrote] there is no category of science which can be called applied science. There is only science and the application of science, related to each other as the fruit is related to the tree that bore it. The great practical inventions, the great achievements of art and industry, even the changes in the intercourse between nations, all originate from the brains of eminent mathematicians, from the laboratories of expert physicists and accomplished chemists, and from the observations of ingenious naturalists.

Scientific engineering in America has, since the beginning of this century, to a magnificent degree applied the principles Pasteur used to employ during his lifetime.

From the start of his researches on the fermentations Pasteur had pointed out the practical advantages industry could derive from his work. The principles he set forth were clear and simple: the purity of a ferment and its free development in a suitable medium are prerequisites of perfect fermentation. In every industry where fermentation plays a part, the microscope is an indispensable tool.

During the year 1861, while he dedicated himself to study the world of microscopic life, Pasteur obtained results that were of enormous consequence for the manufacture of vinegar and the preservation of wines. He went to Orléans to study the manufacture of vinegar. In the process wine is left in contact with air in large open casks; on the surface a pellicle forms known as mother of vinegar or mycoderma aceti. Pasteur recognized that the micro-organisms of which this film consists have the property of fixing the oxygen of the air to the alcohol, transforming it into acetic acid. The manufacturers were convinced that the minute vinegar eels, *anguillulae,* forever swarming in the casks, were necessary for the formation of vinegar. Pasteur taught them otherwise: "This is a grave error. Acetification is hampered by the presence of these little animals." And he went on to explain: "They require oxygen to live, as is proven by their death in bottles filled with vinegar and hermetically sealed. Acetification takes place on the surface of the alcoholic liquid in a thin and frail layer of mycoderma aceti. Suppose there is a strong growth, causing active acetification; then all the oxygen at the surface is used up by the plant, depriving the vinegar eels of it. Unable to breathe, these little worms seek refuge on the walls of the casks near the level of the liquid, where they form a thick white layer of wriggling creatures. That is the only place where they can breathe, and you will understand that they do not want to leave the field to the mycoderma. Quite a few times, in the course of my experiments, I have watched a sort of struggle between the vinegar eels and the organism. As the latter spreads over the surface, the worms gather in clusters underneath and try to drag the mycoderm downward in shreds. In this state it is harmless to them, for we have seen that the submerged plant is practically inactive. Imagine how hard it is for the mycoderma aceti to thrive in the presence of these worms; so if you let them swarm in your vats, the production of vinegar is impeded."

This was not the only advice which Pasteur could give the vinegar-makers; he made practical suggestions for obtaining uniform products in larger quantities. The casks were to be placed in an oven, bringing the temperature to 68–77 degrees F., best suited for the growth of the mycoderma. After filling the casks with wine to which fresh vinegar is added, a pure culture of mycoderm is sown on the surface; it retracts, forming a veil that soon starts to spread, and the process of acetic fermentation is operating.

. . .

Following his researches on vinegar, Pasteur turned to studies on wine, from 1863 to 1864. They were mainly made at Arbois, a short distance from his father's house,[1] in an old café that served as a primitive laboratory. As we learn from Pasteur's collaborator Emile Duclaux, the traditional shop sign was left in the window, and sometimes customers entered to buy food and drinks. Usually they stopped at the door, bewildered by the strange-looking equipment, and left sheepishly. There was no gas in the laboratory; heat was supplied by a charcoal brazier, which was kept going with a pair of bellows. There was no water; it had to be fetched from the public fountain. The utensils were cleaned in the river. The tables were plain boards. In these uncomfortable surroundings Pasteur went to work.

Everybody knows that fermentation of wine takes place in casks that contain the crushed grapes. Pasteur demonstrated that the wild yeasts that convert grape sugar into alcohol are found on the ripe grapes, being deposited there with dust from the air. In addition to these wine yeasts, however, unwelcome parasitic germs are introduced into the vats through the bunches, the hands of the workers, and the presses. They are at first stifled by the fermentation process; unfortunately, once the wine is finished and filled into

[1] This house, kept intact in outward appearance and furnishings, has been converted into a museum.

casks or bottles, they may develop and cause "diseases" of the wine.

Every one of these is related to a particular ferment. Most common is the bitter disease caused by a ferment that affects the noble wines of the Côte d'Or and, to a lesser extent, the common wines of Burgundy, Bordeaux, and the Jura. While all wines are subject to it, only certain types become affected. "In the same way," wrote Pasteur, "epidemic diseases show a predilection for individuals who, by virtue of their constitution or temperament, are predisposed to contract them."

To forestall these maladies of wine—some cause wine to become "ropy" and "oily"—Pasteur devised the method that is now internationally known as pasteurization: the harmful microbes are killed off by heating the wines for several minutes at 55 degrees C. (131 F.). This procedure does not change the taste, and a wine so treated can be stored indefinitely. Thus considerable quantities, up to ten thousand quarts, may be heated and preserved, a boon to wine-growing countries.

After many favorable trials in which he challenged the judgment of connoisseurs, Pasteur deemed it advisable to invite expert dealers who might be able to detect differences in the bouquet of the same wines, heated and unheated. A commission of professional wine-tasters was called, and from November 16 to

November 23, 1865, they sampled twenty-one wines of different vintage; there were wines from Arbois, from Le Cher, from Burgundy, and some blended wines. The members of the commission testified that the differences between the heated and unheated wines were so faint that they escaped nine out of ten of the experts. The consensus was that heating did not alter the quality of the wines in the least: "We cannot praise highly enough the method of M. Pasteur. It appears practical for bottled wines because it is not expensive, and even less so when applied to large quantities." Pasteur, to show that imagination may influence the judgment, was not above using a bit of trickery. He invited the tasters to compare two specimens of wine from the same bottle without revealing the source. Every single member of the commission claimed that there was a difference between the two samples!

In his book *Wine and Its Maladies,* which Pasteur published in 1866, there are many pages that give food for thought to wine-makers. It contains remarks that bear out Pasteur's extraordinary talent for observation, and provides a scientific explanation for certain customary techniques. "The practices of the trade," he stated, "appear sometimes surrounded with magic, but looking closer one notes that they have sprung from reasonable experience and serve some useful purpose." To cite an example: in all countries and at all times the vintners have established a certain relation between the life of the wine and that of the grapevine. They assert that the wine is in ferment at the moment when the grape flowers and again in the the month of August when the grape begins to ripen. They are inclined to believe that these different circumstances exert an identical and mysterious influence on the wine. The explanation is simply that at these periods the temperature in the cellars undergoes variations. "But what of it," wrote Pasteur, "if the peasant believes in a mystery? It's the fact itself which we have to consider because it serves as a guide in certain practices of wine-making." Thus he proved himself a model scientist, whose essential qualities are the ability to observe and to interpret facts.

Despite its remarkable success in the wine industry, pasteurization was attacked from various quarters. And when the effectiveness of the method was eventually recognized, many pseudo-scientists claimed priority. Exasperated by such tactics, Pasteur wrote in his straight-forward manner to M. de Quesneville, editor of the *Moniteur scientifique*:

Let me give you a piece of my philosophy. One day, when I was a candidate for a vacant seat at the Academy of Sciences, in an interview of the kind that is customary in such circumstances, one of the oldest and most dignified members said to me, not without a certain bitterness: "My friend, if they stop speaking disparagingly of you in certain journals, tell yourself that you are slipping." Well, sir, go on denigrating my work and my person, as it is your habit. From your attacks I shall draw encouragement to persevere, and to conclude in your manner: A word to the wise is sufficient.

In our day, it is difficult to understand the opposition against Pasteur's innovation. The term "pasteurization" has become a household word, familiar to every schoolchild from the labels on dairy products. The method, one of the foremost instruments of public health, was found applicable to the greater part of beverages and foodstuffs; but it attained its highest importance in the prevention of milk-borne infectious diseases, such as Malta fever (brucellosis) and bovine tuberculosis.

Pasteur was a passionate man. When he was convinced that he was right, he defended his work tooth and nail. When he became violent occasionally, his outbursts were never directed against his attackers but against the falsehoods they preached. "That temperamental and cutting manner which I find appropriate in the defense of truth," he used to say, "I always regret when it goes beyond the limits of courtesy, and I declare that it is never mixed with hostile feelings against my opponents, as long as I consider them to be in good faith." At the end of his life he remarked, as if to excuse himself: "If I have at times disturbed the tranquillity of your academies by somewhat stormy discussions, it was only because I am a passionate defender of the truth."

This man, so intolerant against adversaries who refused to listen to the truth, was in his private life the gentlest, most affectionate and sensitive individual. As Emile Roux stated: "Pasteur's work is admirable and proves his genius, but one had to live in his house to fully recognize the goodnesss of his heart."

XVI

FROM his researches on fermentation, of which the studies on vinegar and wine were side issues, Pasteur had conceived the notion that the infectious diseases were the work of microscopic agents. "I have not finished all my studies," he said, "and the most worthwhile thing would be to carry them further so as to prepare the path for a serious investigation of the origin of the various diseases." Although he was neither a physician nor a veterinarian, he was anxious to penetrate into the domain of pathology in man and higher animals; intuition told him that with his experimental method he would succeed in solving the vast problem of infections.

In the year 1865 silkworm disease threatened the silk industries of Europe and a large part of Asia. Since 1849 it had been raging in the South of France, causing enormous damage. In that year alone it accounted for losses running into hundreds of million francs. The French Senate was startled by a petition signed by 3,600 mayors, councilmen, and landowners from the silk-producing districts. Jean-Baptiste Dumas was then senator of Le Gard, one of the stricken departments, and it occurred to him to entrust his former pupil Pasteur with the task of exorcising the epidemic. Pasteur declined the assignment, but Dumas insisted: "I am placing great store in having your attention devoted to this problem that affects our district. The misery there far surpasses your imagination." Pasteur reminded him that he never had so much as touched a silkworm. "So much the better," replied Dumas. "Since you don't know anything about the subject, you will have no other ideas than those that come from your own observations."

At last Pasteur gave in: "The memory of your favors," he said to Dumas, "would leave me with bitter regrets if I were to refuse your urgent request. Count on me." By a stroke of luck, such as sometimes benefits superior men, the study of the diseases of silkworms turned out to be for Pasteur the gateway to his pioneer researches in the field of infectious diseases.

On June 6, 1865, Pasteur proceeded to Alès in the Gard department, where the silkworm disease called pébrine had reached disastrous proportions. He learned that the malady was characterized by the appearance, inside the worms and on their skin, of tiny black spots resembling grains of pepper. The affected worms became arrested at different stages of development, and many died in the first stages. The harvest of cocoons was completed; however, a little silkworm nursery, less than a mile from the town, was still operating. Pasteur established headquarters near by.

His first step was to interview the peasants and the

workers in the nurseries. This was his method: before coping with a problem, he used to gather, sift, and survey all the materials that might originate from careful observation. As he stated: "One should not neglect the least little thing; often a remark from the most uncultivated man, provided he does what he does well, is infinitely precious." Soon he noticed a general atmosphere of confusion and pessimism. The articles in trade magazines only added to the trouble of the minds. The silkworm-breeders were despondent because none of the recommended remedies was effective.

Nine days after his arrival in Alès, Pasteur was called to Arbois, to his father's sickbed. He did not find him alive, though. His grief was profound.

I owe him everything [he wrote to his wife] . . . he has instilled into me the habit of work and the example of a most loyal and fulfilled life. . . . You, my dear Marie, did not know him at the time when he and my mother toiled for their beloved children, especially for me, to pay for my books, the months in college, and the study in Besançon. I see him before me, my poor father, in his leisure time from his hard work, reading a great deal, incessantly trying to educate himself, at other times drawing or making wood sculptures. He was devoted to knowledge and learning.

On his return to Alès, Pasteur started to examine crushed sick silkworms under the microscope, and he observed small corpuscles. Two Italian naturalists, Filippi and Cornalia, had pointed out such corpuscles in worms and moths before, and a French naturalist, Quatrefages de Bréau, had mentioned them in an interesting report presented to the Academy of Sciences; however, no importance was attached to these findings. Pasteur had the inspiration that the corpuscles were related to the disease. After examining several groups of silkworms, he did not hesitate to state at the Agricultural Meeting of June 26 in Alès: "The corpuscle is a positive sign of the disease. It is wrong to look for it, as has been done, in the seeds or in the worms; they can carry the germ of the malady without showing corpuscles under the microscope. The disease develops mainly in the chrysalises and in the moths, and this is where one has to look for the corpuscles. There must be an infallible process of procuring healthy seed by selecting moths free from corpuscles."

Despite the wide spread of the epidemic, Pasteur succeeded in finding healthy moths, and he preserved the seeds of these as well as eggs from moths exhibiting corpuscles. He said to himself, let us see what happens next year; if the seed from unaffected moths is healthy, it will prove that one can obtain good breeding batches by selection. But he had to endure vicious criticism. He was told that the Italian Cantoni had already tried reproduction with unaffected moths and had failed completely. "Your selected seeds may produce healthy worms," warned Cornalia, "but these will take sick because of the *genius epidemicus* that reigns everywhere." Pasteur was undisturbed; he continued his studies in his own way.

Whenever he approached a scientific problem, he visualized the solution, so much was he guided by his intuition. But then he used to stop, to control himself carefully, for he had that doubting mind without which a scientist is prone to grave errors. "In the experimental sciences," he said, "one must always have doubts since observations require confirmation. And, above all, beware of undue haste in the desire to finish up; be your own vigilant and tenacious adversary; always think of possible pitfalls."

Pasteur returned to Paris, to the Ecole Normale, in the beginning of September 1865. Another tragedy darkened his family life; his daughter Camille died at the age of two. "My poor child passed away this morning," he wrote to his master Jean-Baptiste Dumas, "to the very end she remained lucid; when her little hands became cold, she kept asking me to put them into mine, something she had never done during her long illness, and until her last breath she spoke with her usual intelligence to those around her."

But this was not the end of Pasteur's sorrows. He

was seeking comfort in his work in Alès when his wife sent word on May 21, 1866, to hurry to Chambéry where his daughter Cécile was gravely stricken with typhoid fever. She died two days later at the age of twelve and a half, and was buried in Arbois.

Pasteur had deeply loved this child, with her sweet face and her serious, almost melancholy mien. He gave vent to his grief in a letter to his wife: "Our beloved children die one after another!" And for the first time he felt despondent: "I am longing to join you, my dearest children!" He resumed his work in Alès, however, with his assistants Maillot and Gernez, who soon were followed by Duclaux. They all lived at Pont Gisquet near Alès, in the open country. Their "ideal house, well-furnished and nicely located on a ravine between two mountains," rented for 600 francs for six months. All around were mulberry bushes, olive trees, and grapevine. A hothouse was converted into a silkworm nursery and laboratory.

Pasteur took charge of everything and even personally went up the mountain to pick mulberry leaves to feed his silkworms. He persuaded a great number of breeders to supervise their breeding stocks. He made considerable progress. He patiently studied innumerable batches of silkworms, and examined the chrysalises, the moths, and eggs one after another under the microscope, looking for corpuscles. He was assisted not only by three co-workers (Maillot,

Gernez, and Duclaux), but also by his wife and his eight-year-old daughter Marie-Louise, who sorted, counted, and unraveled the cocoons.

On June 13, 1866, he wrote the Minister of Public Education: "I have come to the conclusion that there is no actual silkworm disease. This is only an exaggeration of a condition that has always existed, and I believe that one can without difficulties restore the *status quo ante,* even improve on it." He suggested an "infallible" method to obtain healthy seed: depend only on moths that are free of corpuscles. It sufficed to keep the moths isolated, and open and examine each female after it had laid its eggs; if she was found free of corpuscles, one could be sure that the seed was healthy.

In September Pasteur returned to the Ecole Normale, and in January 1867 he went back to Pont Gisquet. His prophecies had come true. The method of selective breeding proved absolutely reliable and working; every female moth was isolated until laying; then it was crushed and examined microscopically. When she was corpuscular, the seed had to be burned. This rather simple procedure saved the silk industry not only in France but also in Austria, Italy, Asia Minor, and in all countries where pébrine was a scourge, and it is employed in silk-producing regions to this day.

It was found that healthy worms could become

sick after ingestion of mulberry leaves soiled with excrements of corpuscular worms; that meant pébrine was both hereditary and contagious. Thus aside from their tremendous practical consequence these studies also held considerable pathological interest. For the first time the origin of a disease in a living creature had been traced to the action of a microbe. For the first time the problems of heredity and infection had been demonstrated in a scientific manner. And for the first time rules for prophylaxis had been established.

Pasteur was convinced that he had reached the goal of his efforts; the cause of pébrine had been found and the evil was conquered by selective breeding. But then a new problem arose: in certain batches of seeds which appeared normal, the worms perished, without showing corpuscles! Pasteur was disconcerted but not discouraged. Again he went to work. He recognized that alongside pébrine another disease was rampant, flacherie, which was located in the digestive tract and usually took a more rapid course.

In the intestines of worms affected with this disease he discovered masses of microbes in form of vibrios (tiny rods), often associated with others arranged like strings of beads.[1] Flacherie was contagious, like

[1] Nowadays, according to the investigations by A. Paillot ("Traité des Maladies du Ver à Soie," Paris, 1930, published by Doin), flacherie is no longer considered a definite morbid entity. This "intestinal disease" of silkworms is attributed in part to Streptococcus bombycis (Pasteur's string-of-beads microbe)

pébrine; worms feeding on leaves that were contaminated with the excrements of sick worms became infected. Strangely enough, the germs were also found in crushed mulberry leaves. How could they become pathogenic? Pasteur conceived the notion that whenever the worms' resistance was weakened, either through faulty breeding conditions (crowding, poor ventilation) or because of climatic factors (thunderstorms, winds, humidity, high temperatures), the germs would thrive in the intestines and become pathogenic. In other words, particular environmental conditions had to be present if the disease was to develop. Furthermore, there was a hereditary predisposition to flacherie, resulting from the debility of the offspring of a sick worm. "If I were a silkworm-breeder," said Pasteur, "I would never hatch a brood from worms without having them observed repeatedly during their last days, to make sure of their vigor and vitality, that is, their agility at the time when they spin the silk."

How inspiring were these remarks on the influence of the environment in the mechanism of diseases! Other observations by Pasteur were to prove no less valuable to man's knowledge of human pathology. For example, Pasteur noted that the vibrios of flacherie reproduce by spores that remain indefinitely in the

in association with a filterable virus, or to Bacillus bombycis (Pasteur's vibrio), also associated with a virus. In the first case, according to Paillot, one is dealing with *gattine*, in the second instance with the *true* (Pasteur's) *flacherie*.

dust of nurseries; this explained how an epidemic could break out after a previous one was extinct for months and even years.

In his work on flacherie Pasteur demonstrated the role of the acquired and of the hereditary biological environment; he explained the revival of epidemics; finally, as in the case of pébrine, he showed how the infection comes about. Thus Emile Roux could make the statement that Pasteur's book on the diseases of silkworms is "a veritable guide to every student of contagious diseases."

Pasteur himself used to tell those whom he chose as his associates: "Read my studies on silkworms; that, I believe, will be a good preparation for the work we are going to undertake."

XVII

AFTER 1865 Pasteur would go to Alès at the beginning of spring, accompanied by his wife and his only surviving daughter, Marie-Louise. The autumn and winter months he spent at the Ecole Normale, where he lived and continued his functions as administrator and director of scientific courses. It was difficult to maintain discipline at the school. One troublesome incident after another occurred. Pasteur was often criticized because he managed the institution in an autocratic manner; he was as severe with others as he was with himself. His attitude was unswerving; he had been entrusted with the mission to keep up discipline, and he fulfilled this ungrateful task with the same exaction with which he inspected flasks and retorts.

In 1867 the school was disturbed by a particularly grave incident, instigated by a speech made by the great critic Sainte-Beuve on June 21. Sainte-Beuve was a liberal, hostile to the imperial regime. He had supported the protest of the people of Saint-Etienne against "the selection of certain works in the foundation of two public libraries." It was scandalous, he exclaimed, that an index of condemned books had been instituted, as in the Catholic Church. The banned books included the *Confessions* of Jean-Jacques Rousseau, and the works of Voltaire, Balzac, Renan, and George Sand.

Sainte-Beuve's discourse rallied the students of the Ecole Normale, the majority of whom opposed the regime. A student named Lallier sent a letter to Sainte-Beuve, in the name of sixty-nine fellow students, congratulating him for having "time and again defended freedom of thought, which was usually ignored and attacked." This letter was published in *L'Avenir national* on July 2. An inquiry was demanded. Young Lallier was suspended by Pasteur. The students protested and asked for clemency on behalf of their comrade. But Pasteur remained adamant.

Unrest spread in the university. The political and literary worlds were stirring. Certain journalists, on the lookout for scandal, declared themselves antagonistic to Pasteur and to the Minister of Public Education, Victor Duruy, who upheld him. Such was the excitement that the two sons of Duruy challenged Jean-Jacques Weiss to a duel because Weiss had attacked their father in the *Journal de Paris*. When Weiss refused to fight, they slapped his face.

This revolt of the school, however, came to an undramatic end. The students were asked to submit their apologies to the minister individually. Only Maspero, who was to become famous for his archeological studies in Egypt, refused to draw up his letter of apology and was listed as resigned. The minister and Pasteur pardoned all the students except Lallier —but he was appointed assistant professor in Sens.

The school was reorganized. The three great leaders—the director Nisard, the director of literary studies Jacquinet, and Pasteur, administrator and director of scientific studies—were relieved of their posts. Pasteur could tell his critics that during the ten years of his administration he had continuously received testimony of the affection and appreciation of his science. Had he only possessed more tolerance of the pranks and exuberance of the young men who loathed the rigid system of regulations, he would have gained the sympathy and confidence of all his pupils, who day after day witnessed his fairness and his devotion to his task. Relinquishing his office, Pasteur could proudly address his students: "During this decade I have not for a single day lost sight of my goal: to make the Ecole Normale Supérieure one of the greatest scientific institutions of our country."

While Pasteur was no longer in charge of the organization and administration of the scientific courses, he still was connected with the school, and a laboratory for physiologic chemistry was being built for him. The construction was undertaken on the initiative of General Favé, adjutant of Napoleon III, who followed Pasteur's work with great admiration.

On his advice Pasteur sent the Emperor a note on September 5, 1865, outlining his research projects:

> Sire, my investigations of the fermentations and of the role of micro-organisms have opened new vistas to the science of biological chemistry. Agricultural industry as well as the medical profession are beginning to reap the benefits; however, the area that still remains to be covered is immense. It is my greatest desire to explore it with renewed energy, without being hampered by a shortage of material resources. When it comes to investigate by patient scientific study those principles that may guide us in discovering the causes of the putrid or contagious diseases, a spacious laboratory with adequate facilities would make it possible to conduct such experiments safely and conveniently. . . .

His wish was granted.

XVIII

ON March 16, 1866, Pasteur traveled again to Alès. He recorded with satisfaction the results obtained through his procedure of examining chrysalises and moths under the microscope. A good many breeders, however, still doubted the effectiveness of his method. When Pasteur warned one of them that his cultures were doomed to failure because all his moths had been found full of corpuscles, he objected that this was impossible since the worms from which the moths had developed were superb. He remained stubborn—and the results of his breeding were miserable. "Enlightened people will soon be convinced and will be the first to confess their error," said Pasteur. "Repentant sinners, they will become fervent apostles."

To his master Dumas he wrote: "You cannot imagine how widespread the corpuscular disease is. The future would look desperate if I had not detected a certain number of broods which are exempt and found that it is easy to reproduce them at will."

Full of zest as always, anxious to convince the unbelievers, Pasteur went to the markets to purchase seeds, which he studied under the microscope. He had moths and chrysalises delivered to him from various nurseries, and in every instance he was able to foretell the outcome of the breeding. He managed to keep the growers on their toes; he gave hope to the small owners whom he saw discouraged. "You think you are helpless against the evil moving in on you," he told them, "but you are wrong. If you have your chrysalises and moths examined under the microscope and learn that no corpuscles have been found, you need not worry, for in your nursery the disease will not turn up." As an example of how simple the technique was, he pointed out that a child, his ten-year-old daughter Marie-Louise, could easily recognize the corpuscles under the microscope.

Along with pébrine, flacherie was also raging. Pasteur advised the growers how to avoid this, too, by watching the breeding closely. "Observe," he told them, "the development of the fourth molt to the cocoon. If you find vigorous-looking worms at that stage, and if the emerging moths are free of corpuscles, have no fear: the seed will be excellent. If you neglect the first rule, you may see flacherie appear; neglect the second, and you may get pébrine. Neglect both—and you may have both diseases at once."

Later Pasteur devised a bacteriological technique for detecting the presence of flacherie in the moths used for production of seeds. The method consisted in "extracting with the point of a scalpel a small portion of the mouth cavity of a moth, then mixing it with a little water and examining it under the microscope. If the moths do not show the characteristic micro-organism, the strain from which they came may be considered as suitable for seeding."

More and more people from everywhere sent seeds, chrysalises, and moths to Pasteur, who became a kind of prophet. "Let me tell you," he said to the mayor of a community of Le Gard, "that your two batches of seeds, coming from very sucesssful broods, and about to be grown in your locality, will be a complete failure, no matter how skillful the breeders are. Last year, it would have taken only five or ten minutes of an easy microscopic examination to recognize that the cocoons, while excellent for spinning, were totally unsuited for breeding, and that the seed of these moths will carry destruction into your community this year." What Pasteur foretold always proved to be true. Eventually the microscope became standard equipment for all intelligent growers.

In the meantime, the dealers in silkworm seeds, disturbed by Pasteur's discoveries, which hurt their trade seriously, resorted to spreading the most vicious and harmful rumors against his method of seed selection. He constantly had to defend himself, to show his opponents that they were wrong. This he did with that vehemence which gripped him every time he was sure of being on the side of the truth and suspicious of the bad faith of his adversaries. As an example, he wrote to the Marquis de Bimard, a silkworm-breeder who had tried to nullify the conclusions of his work:

I want to tell you, Monsieur le Marquis, without malice and with the respect due to your integrity—in which I believe, as you may believe in mine—that you don't know the first thing about my investigations and their results, about the definite principles they have established and their practical implications. Most of them you have not read and the ones that have come to your notice you did not understand.

In August 1868 Pasteur left Paris, where he had been supervising the construction of his laboratory at the Ecole Normale, and went to Toulon to conduct experiments on preservation of wines. The Minister of the Navy had decided to ship great quantities of heated and unheated wines to Gabon and Cochin China to evaluate Pasteur's method. "There is a tremendous potential market for French wines in foreign countries," Pasteur used to say. "At present our ordinary table wines cannot be effectively exported to England and overseas." The frigate *La Sibylle* sailed from Toulon, carrying 650 hectoliters (65,000 quarts) of heated wine and 50 hectoliters (5,000 quarts) of the same wine, untreated. The test was a complete success; only the first lot arrived at its destination unchanged.

Pasteur deserves particular credit for his ceaseless

efforts to achieve close co-operation between laboratory and industry. In contrast to those scientists who remain secluded in their laboratories and take little interest in the utilization of their discoveries, Pasteur invariably took pains to put to the test, and on a large scale, what he had observed in the laboratory. He did so with complete unselfishness; no sooner had he made a discovery that was to bring profit to industry than he secured a patent and then let the process, e.g. the heating of wines, fall into the public domain. As he said, "The scientist must never exploit his own discoveries, otherwise he would not be a free man anymore."

Unfortunately, this period of continued and prodigious exertion was to be followed by terrible days.

XIX

PASTEUR had returned to the Ecole Normale in the beginning of autumn 1868. On Monday, October 19, after breakfast he became aware of a tingling sensation in his left side. Nevertheless he went to the Academy of Sciences. His wife was worried and accompanied him as far as the courtyard of the Institute. He came back to the Ecole Normale with his teacher Balard and his friend, the chemist Sainte-Claire Deville. He went to bed early. The tingling started again; his speech deteriorated, and his left arm and left leg became progressively heavy and powerless.

In the morning, the famous physician Andral prescribed application of sixteen leeches behind the ears. Blood was flowing profusely. Pasteur became very drowsy, but did not lose consciousness. "If I only could cut off this arm which is as heavy as lead," he said with a sigh. By evening his condition seemed hopeless; he was very weak, and was torn between restlessness and apathy. But the following morning his mind was clear. He said to Sainte-Claire Deville: "I am sorry to die, I wanted to do more for my country. . . ."

"I assure you, you are going to recover," Deville

replied. "You will survive me. I am older than you; promise that you will deliver my eulogy." Deville forced a smile, but when he left the room, he burst into tears.

After a week of anguish, while the intellectual circles of the capital were incessantly inquiring about the condition of the patient and while Pasteur's friends kept vigil at his wife's side, hope returned. During the night of October 25, he was able to dictate to his pupil Gernez the outline of an ingenious bacteriological method for detecting seeds predisposed to flacherie. Next morning, Gernez delivered this note to Jean-Baptiste Dumas, who "could not believe his eyes." The same day Dumas read the memorandum to the Academy of Sciences.

Several weeks later, Pasteur resumed work, although his left side remained paralyzed. His forearm was bent and contracted. His fingers were immobilized in a clenched position. His leg was stiff, making walking difficult. In this adversity, Pasteur had the satisfaction of seeing a large and beautiful laboratory building rise in the gardens of the Ecole Normale. But he wondered whether he would ever be able to use it; he wondered whether his vitality and will power would enable him to overcome his infirmity and to continue his life work.

XX

ON December 11, Pasteur wrote to Duclaux: "The time has come to prepare our big expedition to the South. I have already written to the Minister of Agriculture to name as my collaborators Gernez, Raulin, Maillot, and you." He added: "My general health is as good as ever. During the last ten days I have been getting up, or rather I am helped in that. Progress is slow but evident. I have decided to leave Paris in a month."

Between the tenth and sixteenth of January, Pasteur went out twice by carriage, and on January 18 he left Paris, assuring his friends that he would be "less uncomfortable on the train than in a bad fiacre." From Alès a coach took him some twenty miles farther to Saint-Hippolyte-du-Fort, where he intended to watch the preliminary tests of silkworm breeding sponsored by the Agricultural Committee of the Gard department. In this region there was at his disposal only an unheated house, badly arranged and poorly equipped. Here a laboratory was improvised.

From a letter of Pasteur's to Jean-Baptiste Dumas we learn his daily routine. Every morning Gernez, Maillot, and Raulin called on him to prepare the day's schedule. At noon he got up, after breakfasting in bed and listening to the reading of a journal or dictating some letters. In good weather he spent an hour or two in the little garden. When not too tired, he dictated to his wife a page of his forthcoming book on the diseases of silkworms. In the evening his assistants reported on their progress. At half past six he had dinner with his wife and daughter. Afterward he always was overcome with fatigue and felt like sleeping for twelve hours at a stretch, but about midnight he invariably woke up. Not until morning could he fall asleep again for an hour or two. "You see," he wrote, "that I have to be good; besides I am under the steady and strict supervision of my wife and my little daughter, who takes away my books, paper, pens, and pencils without mercy and with a persistence which both amuses and upsets me."

The method of seed selection introduced by Pasteur began to spread in southern France, Italy, and Austria. The results were excellent. Certain trade journals, however, continued to challenge Pasteur's innovation. The articles were signed by ignorant or jealous individuals, or even by seed-dealers who felt cheated because they had imported seeds from Japan at great expense. Twenty million francs, a considerable sum, was quoted for the last year. If one could make use of native healthy seeds, what a loss! Pasteur found little comfort in the adage that sooner or later the truth would prevail. Such attacks hurt him deeply; he could not tolerate bad faith.

An unfortunate accident seemed to interfere with his convalescence; at the end of January he fell on his left side, and this caused him great suffering. He was unhappy because he could not work as before. "The least mental effort," he wrote to Sainte-Claire Deville, "does me in. Yet I have my appetite and I manage a little sleep. If these two restoring forces stay with me, I can hope for better days." Indeed, he felt some improvement during the following weeks; leaning on his wife's arm, he managed to walk for a quarter of an hour, dragging his leg heavily. He was able to move his left forearm slightly, but the hand remained useless.

In April, Pasteur left Saint-Hippolyte-du-Fort to return to Pont Gisquet, near Alès. On July 17 he submitted a report to Napoleon III in which he summed up the results of his studies and demanded fair treatment. He complained how outrageous it was to be criticized by ignorant or selfish individuals when he had worked painstakingly for five years, under most difficult conditions, to bring light where everything had been black. He pointed out that in the years prior to his researches one theory after another had been formulated regarding the cause of the disease and its dissemination across the map of Europe and Asia. Numerous remedies had been recommended, none of which proved effective. And now he was the target of attacks by persons who covered up their failures by repudiating in their articles the results that had eluded their efforts. This is "a common fate of all new discoveries," Pasteur stated with some bitterness.

Jealousy was not the only motive that impeded the general acceptance of Pasteur's method. There were also economic factors involved. The trade in seeds with Japan, as Pasteur underlined in his note, could only last and prosper at the expense of a continuance of the scourge; naturally the companies that were profiting from this business had a strong interest in rejecting the possibility of getting healthy broods from native seeds. "The disloyalty and the maneuvers of the merchants dealing in native seeds are limitless," wrote Pasteur. He demanded of the Emperor that "justice and light should decide on the validity and the practical usefulness" of his studies.

Several weeks after this note was delivered, the Marshal Vaillant, Chancellor of the Court, invited Pasteur to Illyria, several miles from Trieste. There the Imperial Prince owned an estate, the Villa Vicentina, where for years cultivation of silkworms had operated under deplorable conditions. Pébrine was rampant. What a wonderful opportunity for Pasteur to make an extensive test of his method! Without hesitation he accepted the offer. On November 25, 1869, he arrived with his family at the Villa Vicentina.

Pasteur noted that in Lower Austria, Lombardy, and northern Italy there was a strong movement in favor of his work. The salvation of the silk industry, he was assured almost unanimously, rested upon the adoption of his principles. Never had life been so pleasant for him as in this period. In a letter to Jean-Baptiste Dumas he admitted that he "greatly needed peace of mind, removal from the militant and often feverish scientific life in Paris." He realized that it was not so much his work that was harmful to his health as the unwarranted opposition that he foolishly "wanted to silence, something which is often impossible."

For the first time in his career he enjoyed a restful life at the Villa Vicentina. Surrounded by his assistants in a beautiful and spacious laboratory, he went from one to another, discussing their findings. He hoped that some day he would regain the use of his left hand, but it was to remain powerless. "When my head is free," he wrote to Deville, "I forget the past and make projects. But when my head becomes heavy and clogged, I get discouraged and can only think of crawling into a remote corner to die."

He went for walks and took rides in a carriage; he even sometimes walked ponies which had "such nice red pompons" and were the delight of his children,

Marie-Louise and Jean-Baptiste. All over the neighborhood people asked for the honor of being introduced to him, and he was flattered to find that they were well informed about his studies on silkworms. "My countrymen," he wrote, "ought to be ashamed of lagging behind foreigners in the application of the process which they owe me and which in their ignorance they try to belittle."

He completed his book on silkworm diseases. The total cost of its publication—two volumes with numerous plates—was 40,000 francs. At times, as he admitted, he was "very downhearted"; what could he do in such a precarious state of health? And yet he planned great projects.

The effects of sickness on the body [he wrote to his physician, Dr. Godélier] are much like those of the winter on vegetation. When health returns, or when we imagine so, we resemble a plant activated by rising new sap, and we feel capable of doing work that may bear new fruit. Unfortunately, here and there in the middle of the forest one finds trees that hardly grow green again or not at all. Am I one of these? Perhaps you know the answer.

Thus he was torn between hope of new and great undertakings and doubt of himself. "My future ambition," he wrote to Dumas, "will be limited to directing, supervising, and controlling the observations of my collaborators and pupils rather than to work myself. After all, what can one do with only one good hand and a sick brain?"

In June 1870 Pasteur could be certain that his labors at the Villa Vicentina were crowned with complete success. In 35 years no one had seen so many and such perfect cocoons; the crop promised to be abundant as never before. In the beginning of July, Pasteur and his family returned to France via Vienna and Munich. On July 12 he arrived in Strasbourg. The news from Paris was alarming: war with Germany was imminent.

XXI

PASTEUR was an ardent patriot. To the reiterated maxim that science has no country, he used to reply: "Yes, but the man of science must have one." As soon as war was declared, he wanted to enlist in the Imperial Guard. It was hard to dissuade him; but his left arm was paralyzed and his leg was so completely stiff that he could hardly walk by himself. He had to find satisfaction in seeing his son, Jean-Baptiste, enlist as a foot soldier in a battalion of Chasseurs.

From the town of Arbois, where he found refuge on September 5, after the collapse of the Empire, Pasteur watched with agony the outcome of the hostilities. The French defeats made his heart ache. "We must uphold our hope to the last," he wrote, "say nothing which may daunt our courage, and make fervent vows for a prolonged fight to the bitter end. Let's keep up our spirit! Bazaine might yet become our saviour." Alas, then came the capitulation of Bazaine, the surrender of the fortress of Metz—"How I envy the dead!" Pasteur exclaimed in despair.

The siege of Paris followed. On January 18, after the bombardment of the Museum of Natural History by the German army, Pasteur returned his honorary doctor's diploma to the Dean of the Medical Faculty of Bonn University with these words:

When I protest sternly out of my deep respect for you and the distinguished professors who have attached their signatures to the document of your Faculty, I follow the dictate of my conscience in asking you to erase my name from your archives and to take back this diploma, as a token of the indignation aroused in a French savant by the barbarism and the hypocrisy of a ruler who, to satisfy a criminal arrogance, gloats in the massacre of two great nations.

The Italians offered a professor's chair to Pasteur; he could choose between the universities of Pisa and Milan. For a fleeting moment he faltered, fearing that the enemy cannonade might destroy the Ecole Normale and his laboratory. But then he made up his mind and gave this fierce answer: "I would feel as if I had committed a crime and would deserve the penalty for desertion if I were to leave my country now, when it is in distress, seeking abroad the easy comfort that France no longer can offer me."

In his hometown Arbois, Pasteur was fearful of seeing any day the entry of the Prussian conquerors. And he was anxiously awaiting news from his son, Jean-Baptiste, who was fighting in Bourbaki's army. On January 24, 1871, unable to stand the uncertainty any longer, he decided to make his way to the Swiss border where Bourbaki's forces were supposed to be. Accompanied by his wife and daughter, Pasteur arrived in Pontarlier, after a grueling three days' journey over snow-covered roads. The town was swarming with troops. The disorganized soldiery offered a pathetic sight. Suffering from dysentery and frozen feet, the men were in vain seeking shelter from the cold. The news spread that Bourbaki had shot himself through the head. Chaos and misery were all about. A soldier who Mme Pasteur queried about the battalion of Chasseurs among whom her son might be found, answered: "All I can tell you is that of a battalion of 1,200 men only 300 are left."

"You are looking for Corporal Pasteur?" said a passing soldier. "He is alive. I slept next to him last night. He stayed behind, he is sick. Perhaps you'll find him on the road leading to Chaffois."

Pasteur and his wife had hardly passed the gates of Pontarlier when they caught sight of a soldier in a rickety cart, all muffled up, his face showing the marks of grim suffering: it was their son! Pasteur took Jean-Baptiste to Geneva for a few days. Soon recovered from exposure and exhaustion, the youth returned to France to rejoin his unit.

From Lyon, where he stayed for several weeks Pasteur wrote to his pupil Duclaux, the day after the Paris Commune: "My head is brimming with splendid ideas. The war has sent my brain to pasture. I am ready for new projects. . . . Poor France, beloved country, could I only help to restore thee from thy disaster!" Indeed he did, and some years later the great English biologist Thomas Henry Huxley could state: "The discoveries by Pasteur have given back to France the five billion francs demanded by Germany after the war of 1870."

XXII

IN April 1871 Pasteur went to Clermont-Ferrand for a sojourn of a few months. Duclaux was then Professor of Chemistry at the Faculty of Sciences in that town. In near-by Chamalières was a brewery, which Pasteur visited. The idea came to him to study the fermentation of beer, as a follow-up of his previous work on fermentation. What satisfaction would it be if he were able to improve the French beer industry so that it could ultimately compete with the superior German product!

One had to solve, he realized, the problem of cultivating pure yeasts and look into the causes of alterations that make beer turbid, sour, "turned," slimy, and putrid. The studies he had started in Chamalières were continued in Tantonville in the Vosges. Soon he could demonstrate that changes in beer, just like those in wine, are caused by microscopic organisms, either introduced from the air, or by the raw materials, or by the brewing apparatus. When the beer did not contain such microbes it was unchangeable. And just as it was possible to prevent "diseases" of wines by the heating-process, one could avoid spoilage of beer by heating it to 55 degrees C. (131 F.) after bottling.

Pasteur, not content with having established this principle, saw to the utilization of his method, as he had previously done with wines. He designed special apparatus for the breweries. To him the advance of industry was entwined with the progress of science; as he used to say: "Always keep the practical application in mind as your goal, but with the solid and staunch support of the scientific principles on which it rests."

Sometimes Pasteur seemed to possess the gift of vision, as when he made a visit to the old, established Whitbread brewery in London in September 1871. In this giant enterprise the study of yeast under the microscope was entirely unknown. Pasteur asked to perform some studies in the presence of the staff. He examined with his instrument the yeast of the porter beer, collected in an overflow pipe from the fermentation vats. He found filaments characteristic of "turned" beer. "The porter fermentation in the brewery," he said to the manager, "leaves much to be desired." The answer was that on that very day a fresh yeast had been ordered from another London brewery. "If you were familiar with the use of the microscope, you could have prevented the poor condition of your product." Continuing his tests, Pasteur found in a sample of beer three or four filaments per microscopic field. He contended that this beer spoiled readily, that it had to be disposed of immediately for consumption, and that already the taste was inferior. After long hesitation everybody agreed. They fetched a sample of the barm used in the brewing process; it was found full of the noxious filaments.

Then Pasteur inquired about the losses resulting from spoilage. The managers estimated them at 20 per cent of the total production. Abandoning their reticence, they finally admitted that they kept a large quantity of beer that had gone bad less than two weeks after brewing and was positively unfit for drinking. When Pasteur examined it, he could not find any microbes; but then he realized that the beer had obviously cleared through prolonged standing. The now inert micro-organisms should have accumulated at the bottom of the huge reservoirs. He examined this deposit: sure enough, it was an ugly mass of filaments.

A week later, when Pasteur revisited the brewery he was pleased to learn that not only had a microscope been procured without delay but the yeasts for all types of beer which had been subjected to fermentation since his last visit had been changed.

Pasteur's studies of beer were only a sideline of his researches into fermentation. In his reports and in his book entitled *Studies on Beer. Its Diseases and their Causes. Method of Making it Unchangeable,* Pasteur reaffirmed his theory of fermentation as a general biological phenomenon, a consequence of life without air. An enormous wealth of working programs and helpful suggestions are offered in this volume for the benefit of industrialists and experimenters, in addition to analogies valuble to both biologists and physicians. Actually, these prosaic researches were the prelude to Pasteur's dramatic discoveries in the field of infectious diseases.

XXIII

SINCE his first studies of fermentation Pasteur had contemplated investigating the etiology of the contagious diseases, which until then had remained a mystery. Doctors spoke of miasmas, deleterious products, of the "genius epidemicus." Rejecting such vague speculations, Pasteur reasoned that these diseases, like the fermentations, had to be caused by micro-organisms; disintegration of a living being by sickness and decomposition of organic matter through fermentation were certainly related. "As we see gross alterations occur in wine and beer due to microscopic organisms, that have found refuge and thrived in these liquids into which they were introduced invisibly and accidentally, can one help being possessed by the idea that a process of the same order may sometimes take place in man and animals?"

But how could Pasteur approach this problem? He was neither a physician nor a veterinarian. In order to achieve co-operation with the medical world he appealed to the Academy of Medicine, composed of the most illustrious physicians, surgeons, and biologists of France. In 1873 he was elected to the section of free members by a one-vote margin.

There and then commenced a bitter feud between

the defenders of traditional medicine and the protagonist of the new doctrine. From the rostrum of the Academy, Pasteur parried his opponents with passionate vehemence.

"The virulent diseases are within us," said the physicians.

"No," retorted Pasteur, "they originate from germs that are foreign to our body."

"Our organism produces disease," said the traditionalists.

"There is no spontaneous generation," proclaimed Pasteur. "Like the fermentations, contagious diseases are caused by living agents."

It was not only the doctors whom Pasteur took to task; there were also the surgeons who did not dare to operate any more since the slightest negligence could spell disaster; conversation in the surgical wards centered around purulent infection, putrefaction, hospital gangrene. Pasteur startled the surgical specialty by announcing at the Academy of Medicine on January 5, 1874: "If I had the honor of being a surgeon, I would never introduce into the human body an instrument without having passed it through boiling water or, better still, through a flame and rapidly cooled right before the operation." Shortly afterward he reiterated his opinion, pointing to the dangers resulting from microbes, which cling to the surface of all objects. He warned the surgeons: "You should use only instruments and bandages, that have been previously exposed to a temperature of no less than 130–150 degrees C. (266–302 F.) You should use water only after submitting it to a heat of 100–120 degrees C. 212–248 F.)."

The great Scottish surgeon Joseph Lister, a promoter of the antiseptic method (which he introduced under the influence of Pasteur's teachings), praised the results derived from the germ theory: "If you ever come to Edinburgh," he wrote to Pasteur, "I think it will be truly rewarding for you to see in our hospital to what extent the human race has benefited from your work. Do I need to add what great satisfaction it would give me to show you here what surgery owes to you?"

In the years from 1873 to 1876 Pasteur was engaged in an unending fight against official medicine. He was exposed to ignorant, skeptical, often malevolent persons, who attacked his work on fermentation and contagious diseases. In the Academy of Medicine and in the Academy of Sciences, there were stormy discussions in which Pasteur vigorously defended what he knew to be the truth.

One day, exasperated by one of his old colleagues, Poggiale, Pasteur lashed out at him from the platform form of the Academy of Medicine in these words:

". . . What! For twenty years I have labored with this problem, and to think that the right to verify, to control, to discuss, and to interrogate should belong to a man who has done nothing to inform himself, who just has read publications more or less attentively in his studio, with his feet on the rail of the fireplace!"

While Pasteur was more than annoyed by such disputes, he was receiving encouragement from many sides. The great English physician John Tyndall wrote him:

> For the first time in the history of Science we can entertain the certain and definite hope that, inasmuch as the contagious diseases are concerned, medicine will soon be freed of empiricism and placed on a solid scientific basis. When this great day comes, mankind will, I am convinced, gladly acknowledge that it owes the largest share of gratitude to you.

In July 1874, in recognition of his outstanding and unselfish services which had enriched the treasury of France, the National Assembly voted a National Award for Pasteur, in the form of a life pension of 12,000 francs annually. This approximated the salary of the chair at the Sorbonne which he had to give up because of ill health. The physiologist Paul Bert, member of the Assembly, when drafting the proposal of this bill referred to the millions that Pasteur had secured for France "without retaining an iota."

XXIV

ONE clear day in the beginning of 1876, it entered Pasteur's mind that he could render his country greater service if, while continuing his research work, he would uphold the privileges of Science in the Senate. He was one of those fervent patriots who were inspired by the desire to regain for France, on the heels of a lost war, a leading part in the intellectual world. To further this goal, Pasteur wanted to convince the executive powers of the advantages of scientific institutions and the necessity to have industry profit from the discoveries made in the laboratory.

Elections to the Senate were to be held in all of France on January 30, 1876. Pasteur announced his candidacy in the Jura district. His program must have appeared naïve to seasoned politicians accustomed to party intrigues; it was the reflection of his own pure soul. Detours, subterfuges, compromises were alien to him. "Strongly endorsed as a candidate to represent our department in the senatorial elections, I have gratefully accepted the nomination. Now I ask for your vote. I am not a politician. I do not belong to any party. Never having studied politics, I am ignorant of many things, but this I know: I love my country and have served it with all my might; this is my belief." He concluded: "If you honor me with your vote, I shall represent science in all its purity, dignity, and independence in the Senate."

In the course of the campaign he turned out to be a very poor candidate, falling into every trap of his adversaries, not knowing how to deal with hecklers, disconcerted by the interruptions, noises, and various tactics at public meetings, discountenanced by the attacks of newspapers and by certain maneuvers that he stamped as "disloyal." The man who time and again at the Academy of Sciences and at the Academy of Medicine had proved himself as a fiery polemicist and master of crushing arguments was incapable of putting up a defense on the stage of the theater in Lons-le-Saunier where the candidates were reviling each other. The outcome was foreseen; on the day of the elections Pasteur with a mere 62 votes ran far behind the other four candidates. After this resounding defeat Pasteur returned to his laboratory at the Ecole Normale.

In September 1876 an International Congress of Sericulture convened in Milan. France was represented by Pasteur. He was accompanied by his old associates Raulin, Duclaux, and Maillot. The first two were then professors at the Faculty of Sciences in Lyon, the latter was Director of the Institute for Silk Culture at Montpellier.

This congress was a triumph for Pasteur. The majority of the speakers acknowledged that only his method of individual seed selection was effective against pébrine. In the vicinity of Milan Pasteur was pleased to see a silkworm nursery where 70 women were busy doing microscopic examinations. After his visit to this plant he wrote to Jean-Baptiste Dumas: "I have experienced a happiness that compensates me many times over for the frivolous opposition I have encountered for several years from some of my colleagues—when I saw my name in big letters on the façade of this fine establishment; it is a spontaneous tribute by the owner."

At the termination of the congress Pasteur offered a toast that was widely acclaimed. Therein he made these often-quoted remarks: "I am imbued with two deep convictions: the first is that Science has no country, the second—which seems to exclude the first but actually is a direct consequence—that Science is the highest symbol of the country. Science has no boundaries—knowledge is the sacred treasure of all mankind, the torch that illuminates the world. Science is indeed the supreme representative of the country, for in the society of nations the one that holds the leadership in the realm of intellect and ideas, will always rank first."

XXV

THE YEAR 1877 marks the beginning of the great Pasteurian saga, one of the most extraordinary chapters in the history of science. At last Pasteur was approaching the Promised Land; from day to day the veil was lifting more and more. And never was there a happier man, never a scientist more dedicated than Pasteur during the period from 1877 to 1886, when one discovery followed the other.

Until 1877 Pasteur had proclaimed his germ theory before physicians and surgeons, but he had not dared to embark on a systematic study of a contagious disease. Was he entitled to do so? After all, he was a chemist, not a physician. . . . Eventually, though, he decided to go ahead and undertake studies of the disease known as splenic fever or anthrax. The cause of this plague, which killed sheep and cattle by the thousands all over Europe, was a big question mark among medical men. In 1850 the French physician Davaine had seen under the microscope in the blood of animals dead of anthrax tiny immobile rods, but he did not attach any importance to them. In 1863, however, Pasteur's report on butyric ferments prompted him to reconsider and to ask himself whether these microscopic rods, which he now called bacteridia, were possibly responsible for the disease.

In 1876 the eminent German physician and bacteriologist Robert Koch was successful in cultivating these bacteridia. He recommended as culture material the aqueous humor collected from the eyeballs of oxen or rabbits. In this medium the bacteridia multiplied, partly developing into long filaments, showing inside tiny brilliant corpuscles or spores. Inoculation of such material into guinea pigs or rabbits produced the disease as readily as blood from a stricken animal. But despite the observations by Davaine and Koch, medical men were still doubtful about the role of these micro-organisms; they were influenced by the distinguished physiologist Paul Bert, who had maintained that anthrax was caused not by bacteridia but by a soluble toxic substance, then called virus.

In his research on anthrax Pasteur employed the same method that had served him so well in his work on fermentation. He put a drop of blood from an animal felled by the disease into a tube filled with sterilized broth; the germs multiplied. With a drop from this tube he inoculated another, with a drop from this one a third, and so on, up to a hundred times. By such successive transfers the original drop had "been diluted into the oceans," as Emile Roux expressed it. It could no longer be maintained that "a soluble diastatic substance" was the cause of the disease; it had to be the bacteridium.

Objections still were raised against Pasteur's view.

There upon he made an experiment that could leave no room for doubt: he let a culture stand so that the bacteridia accumulated at the bottom of the tube. Animals injected with material from the upper layer of the fluid stayed healthy, while a trace of the deeper layers was fatal. This made it evident that the bacteridium, a living micro-organism, was the exclusive cause of the disease. Here was experimental proof of the germ theory.

An old observation by Jaillard and Leplat, however, was held against Pasteur. These authors had inoculated rabbits with blood from a cow, a victim of anthrax, and the animals had perished without showing bacteridia in their blood. Pasteur provided a rational explanation. Immediately after death, the infected animal swarms with bacteridia; some hours later, intestinal microbes, particularly the septic vibrio, invade the blood stream so that now two kinds of germs are present; again some time afterward, the bacteridia disappear and only the septic vibrios are left. Therefore, if one uses the blood immediately after death, one injects the anthrax germs. If one withdraws blood somewhat later, one injects bacteridia together with septic vibrios. Still a while later, one injects only septic vibrios. Jaillard and Leplat had taken an animal that had been dead twenty-four hours; thus they had inoculated the septic vibrio and not the anthrax bacteridium. The former is not abundant and is difficult to see; that is why the authors had not found any microbes in the blood of their rabbits.

On studying this septic vibrio Pasteur demonstrated that it is similar to the vibrios of putrefaction and those of flacherie, which he had described in previous years. He grew this microbe under absence of air: it was anaerobic. Culture material produced a gangrenous septicemia (nowadays called gas gangrene) in inoculated animals.

These findings ought to have convinced the unbelievers, and yet Pasteur remained the subject of criticism by physicians and veterinarians. One of the most implacable was Colin, Professor of the Veterinary School of Alfort. His stand against the germ theory, especially against the microbial etiology of anthrax, led to one of the most stirring episodes in Pasteur's life. The dispute mounted in bitterness from day to day. Inflamed by Colin's unfounded objections Pasteur flung these words into his face from the platform of the Academy of Medicine: "When in the course of a scientific discussion an opponent resorts to this kind of speech, it seems to me that he is no longer a free man since he cannot control his temper. However, between M. Colin and me it is not the form of the debate that matters, it is the basis, the intention that one must question. M. Colin's intention is clear for all to see: he would like to discredit a number of my works which are not under consideration, including even the diseases of silkworms of which he knows nothing. I beg to inform him that these studies defy his criticism, as several of his defy mine a bit."

In the course of one of his controversies with Colin, Pasteur made a classic experiment that demonstrated the influence of the terrain on the development of disease. He had asserted that birds, particularly fowl, did not contract anthrax. Colin contradicted. Several weeks later, he entered Pasteur's laboratory. Before even greeting him Pasteur asked: "You wanted to show me a hen with anthrax. Where is it?"

"You can trust me," said Colin, "you'll have it next week."

Pasteur left for Arbois. Soon after his return, at the first meeting of the Academy, he cornered Colin: "And where is my hen which was supposed to die of anthrax?"

Colin answered he would get it in a few days. Weeks went by, not without repeated reminders by Pasteur and renewed promises by Colin. At last Colin admitted from the platform of the Academy that he had been wrong, that he had failed in his attempt to infect two hens with anthrax although he had injected them repeatedly with blood full of germs. And amidst the laughter of the Academicians he added: "Perhaps I would have succeeded in the end, but I am afraid the cage was not safe, so a voracious dog has terminated the experiment by devouring the two birds."

Amused, Pasteur promised he would show him that it was possible to give anthrax to hens. At the next meeting he actually presented a hen that had died of anthrax. The solution? Pasteur and his collaborators Joubert and Chamberland had hit upon the idea that the resistance of fowl to anthrax might be explained by the fact that the body temperature of these animals is some degrees higher than that of susceptible species. If one would immerse a hen after inoculation with anthrax bacteridia in cold water, thus lowering the temperature, she might contract the disease. No sooner was the experiment devised than it was realized. Full success—in the morning after the injection the hen was dead, full of anthrax germs.

A commission was appointed by the Academy to verify the startling observations by Pasteur. After repeated experiments, it confirmed his statements. Colin, who took part in the proceedings, was compelled to admit his error.

XXVI

PASTEUR was now working feverishly, and every day gave proof of the fecundity of his concepts when applied to medical science. However, there was no let-up in the attacks of his opponents; incessantly he had to defend his views by referring to his previous results.

In July 1878 the famous chemist Berthelot published an unfinished manuscript by the just deceased Claude Bernard. It concerned alcoholic fermentation. Claude Bernard had wondered whether the alcohol derived from grape juice was the product of a soluble ferment, originated in the grapes themselves, rather than due to a living ferment, as Pasteur claimed. In the opinion of Duclaux, Pasteur "could have answered with that Olympian repose which Bernard certainly would have displayed under similar circumstances," but he had too much fighting spirit to remain indifferent. Hardly had he read the memorandum when he started out for Arbois to conduct a strange experiment that would shatter Bernard's theory.

In a previous study he had demonstrated that bunches of unripe grapes do not yet contain any yeast cells. If, he said to himself, I enclosed the vine-plant at a stage where the grapes are still green in hermetically sealed hothouses and, as added precaution, covered the grapes and stems with sterile cotton, I would in October, at harvest time, have plants with ripe grapes free from outside yeasts. These grapes, when crushed under the necessary precautions, would neither ferment nor produce wine. He would take pleasure in demonstrating them in Paris at the Academy, and offer some to his confreres who then would be finally convinced that yeasts were essential to the fermentation of grape juice.

As always, his intuition had not misguided him; his prophecy materialized. On October 10, he made a comparative test with grapes that had been left in the open, and with those that had been enclosed and wrapped in cotton. The result surpassed his expectations: the tubes containing exposed grapes were fermenting after 36 to 48 hours when kept in an oven at a temperature between 25 and 30 degrees C. (77–86 F.), while not a single one of those containing the isolated grapes showed signs of fermentation. This decisive experiment entitled Pasteur to arrive at very daring and yet justifiable conclusions regarding the prevention of contagious diseases:

What thoughts arise from these results! The deeper one penetrates into the experimental study of germs, the more one is struck by unexpected brightness and by amazing revelations of the nature of contagious diseases! . . . These few cubic yards of air, these few square yards of soil (covered with glass), in the midst of a possible universal contagion, were safe from it for several months. So we may assume, by analogy, that some day simple preventive measures can end those scourges that suddenly ravage and terrorize entire populations, such as that murderous yellow fever which recently has invaded Senegal and the Mississippi valley, or that dreadful bubonic plague which is raging on the banks of the Volga!

The digression induced by Claude Bernard's skepticism [1] retarded Pasteur's researches on the etiology of diseases but he resumed them in autumn with his loyal co-workers Chamberland and Roux. From then on every day confirmed his epoch-making germ theory. A good many doubting individuals were finally convinced by his unerring experiments, his irresistible logic, and his indomitable faith in the truths he came to reveal.

[1] In this connection it should be mentioned that it would be wrong to assume that Pasteur disclaimed the existence of diastases or soluble ferments, that for him existed only formed ferments (yeasts, molds, bacteria).

"Like others," he wrote in his *Critical Evaluation of a Posthumous Note by Claude Bernard on Fermentation*, "I believe in the importance of the action of substances which are called soluble ferments; I would even accept that every fermentation is caused by a ferment of this kind . . ."

XXVII

IN May 1879 Duclaux, who worked in Pasteur's laboratory, was suffering from furunculosis. Immediately Pasteur drew some pus from a furuncle (a boil) of the neck. Some days later, he obtained pus from a second and third boil. These specimens were placed in sterile broth, and each time Pasteur noticed development of a microbe consisting of round dots, arranged in clusters. This organism which Pasteur named "bunch of grapes" (staphylococcus) was subsequently found in other persons affected with boils. Injection of culture material under the skin of guinea pigs or rabbits caused formation of small abscesses, containing the same microbe. Thus it was proven that furuncles were due to this germ.

A few months later, the surgeon Dr. Lannelongue took Pasteur to the Trousseau Hospital to see a twelve-year-old girl who was afflicted with osteomyelitis of the tibia. When the surgeon had exposed the bone, Pasteur collected the pus that was oozing out. On microscopic examination he saw masses of a microbe identical with that of furunculosis, and he cultivated it. He came to the conclusion that osteomyelitis was "the furuncle of bones."

Another discovery was to follow, that of the cause

of the dreaded childbirth fever or puerperal sepsis. One day at the Academy of Medicine a doctor was elaborating in vague terms on the etiology of epidemics that occurred in the maternity wards, killing a large percentage of mothers.

Pasteur interrupted him, "What causes the disease is nothing of the kind; it's the physician and his staff who carry the germ from a sick woman to a healthy one."

"Well, I am afraid," answered the speaker, "that this microbe will never be found."

At that Pasteur limped to the blackboard and sketched the diagram of a microbe, shaped like a string of beads (streptococcus). "There—that's what it is like!" he exclaimed.

He felt sure of his contention. A few days before, at the Obstetrical Service of Dr. Hervieux, he had seen a pregnant woman, stricken with puerperal fever. A drop of blood taken from the left index finger had been placed into sterile broth; no growth appeared. But when a new culture was made with blood obtained by another puncture, a microbe developed in the shape of strands of beads. Eighteen hours before the death of the patient a culture tube was inoculated with blood taken from the foot, and again it was soon teeming with microbes. At the autopsy a great quantity of pus was found in the abdominal cavity and in the womb; this as well as blood from the femoral vein was cultivated, and again the "string of beads" microbes were isolated.

"Nowadays it is hard to imagine," wrote Emile Roux, "the state of surprise, even stupefaction that befell doctors and students when Pasteur, with a simplicity and assurance amazing in a man who for the first time visits a maternity ward, criticized the methods of bandaging and insisted that the linen had to be sterilized in an oven."

In March 1879 the dreaded plague had appeared in Russia in the Astrakhan district. It threatened to invade Europe. Pasteur, without having studied the disease, explained at a special session of the Academy of Medicine how one should deal with the problem.

If I were called upon to study the plague where it is raging, I would start from the conjecture—for all research work must start with a tentative idea as a guide—that the plague is due to the presence and development of a germ. From then on I would concentrate on making cultures of blood and of the various body fluids, gathered before or shortly after the death of a victim, with a view to obtaining the microbe in pure form. [And he added a warning against what bacteriologists nowadays call "secondary infection," accompanying the causative germ.] While one has to devote greatest attention to the effects of the disease, one must guard against overrating the weight of this analysis because a number of circumstances may introduce certain micro-organisms into the body of a patient dying or dead of plague. . . .

In the present state of our knowledge the proof that a microbe is, by virtue of its development, the cause of sickness or death becomes conclusive only if this germ has been obtained by successive, indefinitely repeated cultures, and that these are always and invariably capable of transmitting the disease.

Pasteur was incessantly asked to study this or that disease. His laboratory was a beehive of activity. He could only work, however, in silence and concentration. Therefore he did not admit intruders to his laboratory, not even his friends. If someone crossed the threshold and tried to interrupt him, he told him bluntly that he was busy and could not be disturbed. Emile Roux mentioned that one day Pasteur called on the chemist Wurtz at the Faculty of Medicine. He found him amid his students and several visitors, the laboratory buzzing with talk and coming and going. "How in the world," he exclaimed, "can you work in this hubbub?" And when Wurtz replied that it stimulated ideas, Pasteur retorted that it would dispel his.

His diversified researches did not prevent him from continuing his studies of anthrax in the pastures of La Beauce. Fertile as his imagination was, he sometimes permitted it to stray, but he always made sure that a hypothesis was confirmed or refuted by experimentation. One day a farmer showed him one of the fields that were named "cursed fields," because all sheep grazing there contracted anthrax. There seemed to be no explanation. Pasteur looked the pasture over carefully. He observed a multitude of tiny mounds of the sort thrown up by earthworms. Pasteur asked the man whether he had buried carcasses of afflicted animals in the field. The farmer admitted that he had done so, but years ago and deep in the ground.

"Well," said Pasteur, "the worms burrowing to the surface are probably laden with spores that are contained in these little mounds which you see." With these words he scooped up some of the casts and took them to his laboratory. When this material was inseminated into culture broth, the bacteridia of anthrax developed. Pasteur's intuition had not failed him!

XXVIII

PROTECTION of mankind from contagious diseases was the predominant idea of Pasteur. He never ceased to tell his co-workers Chamberland and Roux: "We must find out how to immunize against the diseases of which we have isolated the virus. Just as one can protect man from smallpox, why shouldn't we protect him from other epidemic diseases?" A good many hypotheses were advanced, many experiments tried; Pasteur always followed the course of his imagination, exploring every lead.

For months on end, as documented by his records of experiments, he pondered the relation between smallpox and vaccine. Wasn't the vaccine virus the attenuated virus of variola? Wouldn't it be possible to find for every contagious disease an attenuated virus that would protect against the lethal germ? After many groping experiments there finally came the day of enlightenment. An epidemic disease raging in the barnyards was under study in the laboratory. Normal chickens inoculated with the microbe of this chicken cholera perished within 24 to 48 hours. During the vacation of 1879 Pasteur, before leaving for Arbois, had entrusted the care of his cultures to Chamberland

and Roux. However, they, too, took a holiday, leaving the cultures for several weeks unattended in a cupboard. Upon their return, they injected a hen with an old culture of chicken cholera, and to their amazement the animal remained completely indifferent. Some days later, when they inoculated the same hen with a new 24-hour culture they found that this injection was like the first one tolerated without ill effects, while all other chickens inoculated with the same culture perished. Chamberland and Roux were dumfounded. They were also uneasy. What would they say to their master on his return? Pasteur was not one to condone the least carelessness in working. But they had to tell the truth, and, as Dr. Roux told me, they were afraid of Pasteur's reaction.

"Keep quiet!" Pasteur gruffly said. After a minute of contemplation he exploded: "Well, everything explains itself—this hen has been immunized by being injected with an old culture!"

What Pasteur's genius had perceived in a flash of intuition required months to verify. The question was how a virulent microbe was modified by aging to the point that it became harmless to an animal into which it was injected. Pasteur assumed that air, or rather the oxygen in it was responsible, and that the degree of attenuation was in proportion to the time factor (the older the culture, the more its virulence was lessened). It was amazing to find that the virulence of the microbe appeared "fixed," i.e. the attenuation was transmitted unchanged to successive generations. These observations led to far-reaching implications. Jenner had succeeded in combating a pernicious disease, smallpox, by his vaccination with a mild localized infection, cowpox. While his method protected only against one disease, would it be possible to establish a general principle and to obtain a "vaccine" to ward off all or most infectious diseases and thus give protection to mankind?

Pasteur had arrived at the zenith of his career; "ever-widening horizons" opened before his eyes. He had discovered the agents of infectious diseases and had become their master; he had tamed dangerous microbes and turned them from killers into benefactors. He should have been able to pursue in serenity his triumphant course. The discussions at the Academy of Medicine, however, did not cease. One between Pasteur and Jules Guérin, an octogenarian, was particularly heated and almost led to a duel. From the rostrum of the Academy Pasteur challenged Guérin: "In certain conversations M. Guérin has bluntly stated that he would tear down my work. Now that we are both present we shall see which one, he or I, will come out of this struggle battered and beaten." He added: "M. Guérin has gone further; he wanted to get from me the secret—which I am safeguarding with scientific prudence—of preparing the attenuated virus of chicken cholera. He will not succeed, for he has no right to make such a demand. . . . This is a matter of scientific honor. I am not going to compromise mine by a premature publication just to satisfy the indiscreet, untimely, and unsound curiosity of M. Guérin. I am ready to justify this statement before the Academy if so desired."

At these words Guérin jumped from his seat and started to lunge at Pasteur. The meeting was dissolved in tumult. The next morning Guérin, still raging, sent two seconds to challenge Pasteur to a duel. Pasteur referred them to those whom he considered as "natural seconds" for himself as well as for Guérin: the perpetual and the annual secretaries of the Academy. To the President he wrote that it had not been his intention to offend a confrere, and that in all discussions of this kind he had no other object in mind than the defense of the accuracy of his work.

Pasteur was governed by the idea that attenuation of the virulence of a given microbe was a general biological law. Consequently, one should be able to decrease the virulence of the anthrax bacteridium and thereby obtain an effective vaccine. But here a difficulty arose. The anthrax germs produced spores; these typical forms of resistance remained unmodified and virulent after exposure to the oxygen of the air during aging. Was a vaccine then impossible? To Pasteur no obstacle was insurmountable. After many trials he found the way to prevent the bacteridia from forming spores: he cultivated them at 42–43 degrees C. (107–109 F.). At this "high-fever" temperature the bacteridia, without spores, were just as easily attenuated as the microbes of chicken cholera. They maintained the modification in successive generations when cultivated between 30 and 40 degrees C. 86–104 F.). At that temperature they produced new spores that fixed the virulence. The anthrax vaccine had been discovered—and it proved successful in laboratory tests.

The Agricultural Society of Melun proposed to Pasteur a public demonstration of his immunization method. The program of this "field trial" was drafted by Pasteur himself on April 28, 1881. In the countryside 25 sheep were to be vaccinated and subsequently inoculated with anthrax, at the same time as 25 control animals. The first series was to be resistant while the controls would succumb to the disease. It was an exceptionally severe test, leaving no room for contingencies. But Pasteur dared to seek complete victory. Colleagues and friends around him were uneasy; he reassured them because "what succeeded with 14 sheep at the laboratory would work as well with 50 at Melun."

The animals were gathered at near-by Pouilly-le-Fort, on a ranch belonging to the veterinarian Rossignol, who had initiated the project. Two vaccinations were given, one on May 5 with a highly attenuated microbe, the second on May 17 with a more virulent germ. Every day Chamberland and Roux inspected the animals. Among the agriculturists, veterinarians, and physicians who followed the scientific show with passionate interest, skeptical and hostile elements were in the majority. As Dr. Roux reported: "they considered it an unexpected opportunity to have Pasteur and his assistants drawn from their laboratory to confound them in the broad daylight of a public experiment."

On May 31 veterinarians and spectators met at the farm to watch Dr. Roux perform the inoculation of the most virulent anthrax bacteridium into all the sheep, vaccinated and unvaccinated. Before this happened Colin, the unrelenting adversary of Pasteur, had warned the onlookers: "You have to be wary. You see, there are two parts in the culture broth, a harmless overlayer, and the deeper, really active part. There the bacteridia, by virtue of their weight, have settled and accumulated at the bottom of the container. They are going to inoculate with the upper part the vaccinated sheep which will survive while the controls will be injected with the sediment that will kill them." He asked one of his colleagues to grab at the proper moment the flask containing the infective material and to shake it thoroughly so that the suspension would be uniformly virulent.

Dr. Roux finished the inoculation of the 50 sheep, and a rendezvous was agreed upon in two days, to record the results. The next day Roux and Chamberland observed that some of the vaccinated animals had an elevated temperature. At this news Pasteur was deeply shaken; for a while, as Roux said: "his faith was faltering as if the experimental method might betray him." Mme Pasteur, confident, did her best to encourage him. But Pasteur was full of apprehension; if the experiment failed it would mean the collapse of his germ theory.

"I wished," he said to his wife and his collaborators who rallied around him, "I could crawl into a dark corner. This will be the ruin of all my work and of all my hopes!"

The night passed in anxiety. What news would the next day bring? At nine o'clock in the morning a telegram arrived from Melun: of the non-vaccinated sheep 18 were dead, the others dying. The vaccinated animals were up and around. The closing words were: Stupendous success! When Pasteur reached Pouilly-le-Fort several hours later, 22 unvaccinated sheep were lying dead on the ground, two others were about to die; the last one, panting, showed signs of infection. The 25 vaccinated animals were in fine condition. Pasteur was greeted by an enthusiastic crowd, raving about the "miracle." There was no Doubting Thomas left.

One veterinarian who had bitterly opposed Pasteur exclaimed that he wished to be vaccinated on the spot and then be inoculated with the most virulent anthrax germ. Pasteur turned to another veterinarian: "Haven't I read in a magazine article with your signature, regarding a micro-organism which I recently discovered in saliva; 'Come on! Still another microbe! When we get to a hundred, we'll make a cross'?"

"True," admitted the veterinarian, "but I am a converted and repentant sinner."

"Well," said Pasteur, "let me remind you of the word of the Gospel that Heaven rejoices more over a repentant sinner than over ninety-nine ordinary people."

"I can bring you another one," said a second veterinarian, "it will be M. Colin."

"You are mistaken," said Pasteur, "that man contradicts for the sake of contradicting and does not believe because he will not believe."

The experiment of Pouilly-le-Fort had tremendous repercussions in the scientific world and firmly established Pasteur's authority in the hearts of the general public.

Having conceived a method of attenuating at will the germs of chicken cholera and anthrax, Pasteur wondered whether it would be possible to restore the lost virulence. He noticed that the microbe of chicken cholera, modified to the point of being harmless to fowl, regained its virulence when inoculated into small birds; after passages through canaries, sparrows, and then pullets the strain became again so virulent that it killed hens. As to anthrax, the virulence of an attenuated bacteridium could be increased by passing it through a new-born guinea pig, then through a somewhat older guinea pig, and so on; in this manner the virulence was reactivated until it was strong enough to kill a sheep. Thus Pasteur was successful in modifying the virulence of micro-organisms at will, a remarkable achievement of bacteriology.

Ever since Pasteur had suffered a stroke, his physicians implored him to slow down, but he would not hear of it. The drive for discoveries in the part of the universe he wanted to explore gave not a minute's respite to his exalted reverie; he was possessed with his work. Fortunately, there were two persons to watch over him: his wonderful wife and companion and his devoted son-in-law, René Vallery-Radot, who accompanied him day after day to the academies, scientific meetings, or conferences. Sometimes René waited for hours to take him home to his residence at the Ecole Normale.

The new world that Pasteur had dimly envisaged for twenty years unfolded before his eyes, transcending his imagination. He roamed through it with enthusiasm, eager to communicate his beliefs to those who were drawn to him. A legend, originated by people who did not know him, pictured him as a difficult character, cloaked with an authority that precluded any contradiction. Those who became well acquainted with him, however, were surprised to find a simple man of exceptional goodness. Only when the scientific truth was at stake did the same man prove to be adamant. His modesty was proverbial. An example was provided at the occasion of the International Congress of Medicine in London in August 1861. Pasteur attended the opening session in the company of his son-in-law. He was asked to mount the platform. The audience recognized him instantly and received him with thundering applause. Pasteur turned to his son: "Undoubtedly the Prince of Wales has arrived. We should have come sooner."

"But it's you whom everybody acclaims!" said the President of the Congress, the surgeon Sir James Paget.

When Paget mentioned the name of Pasteur in his discourse, the audience gave an ovation to the French scientist. "I was very proud inwardly," wrote Pasteur the same evening to his wife, "not for myself—you know how I feel about triumphs—but for my country. I appreciated that I was so exceptionally honored amid this enormous assembly of foreigners, especially Germans, who are here in large numbers."

Referring to this extraordinary acclaim throughout the term of the Congress, Dr. Guéneau de Mussy wrote to Pasteur, on August 15: "I have been happy indeed to witness your triumph. You elevate us in the eyes of the world."

Returning to France, Pasteur learned that cases of yellow fever had occurred on the steamer *Le Condé* which, coming from Senegal, had just arrived at Bordeaux. He hurried to this city. When his friends warned him against the danger of infection, he answered: "Life in the midst of danger is the great life, the life of sacrifice, of example and reward." Unfortunately, Pasteur was not able to do any research in Bordeaux; the diseased persons who had survived the voyage were all convalescing.

He awaited the arrival of another ship, the *Richelieu,* which had sailed from Saint-Louis in Senegal. He expected her to have aboard victims of the dreadful disease, as had been signaled on passing Tenerife. But Pasteur had another disappointment; when the *Richelieu* berthed on September 27, she had no more sick men aboard. "Why didn't I get a chance!" wrote Pasteur to his wife. This journey to Bordeaux had been another episode in his life, which was so filled with labor that he once made the statement: "I would feel that I had been stealing if I were to spend a single day without working."

XXIX

RABIES (or hydrophobia) had always been a dreaded disease; the mere word plunged man into terror. Pasteur decided to study and combat it, and he started his experiments in 1880 with Emile Roux. His previous work had taught him that in order to determine the cause of an infection, he had to isolate the responsible germ, cultivate it, and reproduce the disease with it. In the case of rabies, however, no microbe was to be found—or was it invisible? Was his method for once failing?

Pasteur was not discouraged. He and Roux tried to transmit hydrophobia to dogs by inoculating them under the skin with the froth from a mad dog. The sickness appeared, but in an irregular manner: the incubation was always very long and of unpredictable duration. How could one experiment under such conditions?

Since rabies was a disease of the nervous system, Pasteur said to himself, a live micro-organism had to be present in the brain and in the spinal cord. To transfer the disease with certainty and in a short time, would it not be best to make an inoculation from the spinal cord of a rabid dog directly to the surface of the brain after trepanation of a healthy dog? This procedure offered the solution to the problem; all dogs injected in such manner contracted rabies after an interval of about two weeks. The new technique made experimentation possible, and it was soon successfully applied to rabbits.

In June 1881 several members of the Académie Française advised Pasteur to become a candidate. One of the 40 seats was vacant since the demise of Emile Littré, who had been known for his *Dictionary of the French Language* and had been the uncontested leader of the Positivist School after the death of its founder, Auguste Comte.

The success of Pasteur's candidacy seemed assured. He was backed by Alexander Dumas fils, Nisard, Boissier, Caro, the Duke of Broglie, and the Count of Falloux. But Pasteur felt rather embarrassed: How could he deliver the eulogy of his predecessor, his philosophical concepts being in complete contrast to those of Littré?

My philosophy comes from the heart and not from the intellect, [he had written once] and I adhere to that which is inspired by the natural eternal sentiments one feels at the sickbed of a beloved child breathing his last. In that supreme moment, something deep in our soul tells us that the universe is more than an arrangement of certain compounds in a mechanical equilibrium, arisen from the chaos of elements by a gradual action of Nature's forces.

The election took place on December 8. Pasteur's sponsors were Jean-Baptiste Dumas and Nisard. He received 20 out of 33 votes. On April 27 the ceremonial reception was held under the Dome. In his acceptance speech, Pasteur took issue with the Positivist doctrine:

Everybody who believes in the existence of the Infinite—and no one can escape it—focuses in this affirmation more metaphysical contents than are found in the miracles of all religions; for the concept of Infinity has that twofold character of imposing itself upon us and of transcending comprehension. When we become conscious of it, we must bend our knees. Again, in this moment of poignant anguish, we must ask our reason to pause. All the resources of the intellect come to naught, and we are almost overcome by the sublime folly of Pascal. This absolute and primordial idea Positivism sweeps away fallaciously, as well as its consequences for the life of societies. . . . The idea of God is a form of the conception of Infinity. As long as this mystery is pressing on the human mind, temples will be erected for the cult of the Infinite, whether God is called Brahma, Allah, Jehovah, or Jesus. And on the pavement of these temples we see men on their knees, prostrated, overwhelmed by the idea of Infinity.

The great writer and philosopher Ernest Renan answered Pasteur. His speech, in contrast to the profound and affirmative discourse by Pasteur, had various shades of meaning; it was scintillating and meandering. The two men were of entirely different caliber; Renan was a skeptic while Pasteur, having no sense of humor, was unable to understand the subtle grace and the irony of Renan's mind.

This academic meeting had a resounding echo in the intellectual circles of France. Acknowledging Pasteur's discourse as a profession of faith, they admired his courage and his sincerity, which forever made him lay bare his thoughts and feelings. Pasteur was definitely opposed to materialism; as his son-in-law, René Vallery-Radot, pointed out, he "believed in the divine impulse which has created the Universe; with the yearnings of his heart he proclaimed the immortality of the soul." Pasteur respected the religion of his forefathers; he had profound Christian ideals, but he was not, as has been asserted, an observant Catholic.

While Pasteur was a mystic who refused to "die like a vibrio," while he was convinced that the "force" that is in every human being would become "transformed" after death, he was far from being influenced by such reflections in his scientific work. He did not admit religion to the laboratory. When narrow-minded opponents accused him of having approached the problem of spontaneous generation with preconceived ideas, Pasteur replied:

Here neither religion nor philosophy, neither atheism, nor materialism are concerned. I could even add that to me as a scientist this is irrelevant; it is solely a question of facts. I have attacked the problem without preconceived ideas; indeed I was so willing to declare that spontaneous generation exists—had the experiments forced such admission—that I just as readily can now state my final conviction that the followers of this theory are blindfolded.

Regularly Pasteur attended the Thursday sessions of the Académie Française. Sitting next to Alexander Dumas fils, he enjoyed the pleasant discussions about this or that word in the *Dictionnaire,* so different from the acrimonious disputes at the Academy of Medicine. Dumas took these meetings far less seriously. One evening, he amused himself making a beautiful paper hen, and when Pasteur asked for it, to give it to his granddaughter, Dumas handed it to him, after scribbling on one wing: "One of my Unknown Heroines."

Pasteur expressed his respect for the Académie when he welcomed the savant Joseph Bertrand under the Dome on December 10, 1885:

Despite the criticism which the Académie can smile at—remembering that since the days of Bossuet, La Fontaine, and La Bruyère it was blamed as no longer being in the literary movement—one can declare that all the qualities of our race are centered in the Académie Française. . . .

XXX

THE ADMISSION to the Académie Française was but another interlude in the scientific activities of Pasteur. Every day presented new problems. The following episode illustrates the extent of his perspicuity. The professors of the Veterinary School of Turin wanted to test the efficacy of the anthrax vaccination. With the blood of a sheep killed by anthrax, they inoculated a series of vaccinated and unvaccinated sheep. All the animals perished. This result seemed to demonstrate the ineffectiveness of the immunization against anthrax.

As soon as Pasteur learned of this observation, he wrote, on April 16, 1882, to the Director of the Turin Veterinary School to inquire about the exact date of the death of the animal from which the infective blood had been taken. He was informed that the sheep was found dead on the morning of March 22, and that its blood had not been used until the next day. Pasteur also ascertained that in spring an anthrax-ridden sheep, when dead for more than 24 hours, has septic vibrios in his blood. Thereupon he presented his opinion before the Central Veterinary Society of Paris. He stated that the commission of the Turin School had made a serious mistake in its experiment, in so far as it had employed blood of a sheep which was dead for 24 hours, containing, unbeknown to the experimenters, septic vibrios and anthrax bacteridia at the same time.

The experts in Turin, offended by this reproach, tried to refute it with vehemence and irony in a circular letter that was sent simultaneously to Pasteur and to the scientific journals of Europe, stating: "We consider it miraculous that you, from distant Paris, have been able to recognize with certainty the disease that has taken such a toll of our sheep, vaccinated and unvaccinated."

Pasteur answered that he was prepared to come to Turin. "You will in my presence," he advised them, "inoculate as many sheep as you please, with virulent anthrax germs. In each case the time of death will be recorded. I shall prove that without exception the blood of the carcasses which at first contains only anthrax germs, will on the following day be full of septic vibrios and bacteridia. Day by day, a written protocol will be kept of the proceedings, to be made public afterward through the academies of Turin and Paris." Unfortunately, the professors of Turin did not consent to what they called a challenge. An exchange of rather sharp letters ensued, and the experiment that would have convinced the Italians of their error never materialized.

. . .

Like all summers, the summer of 1882 was spent in Arbois. Every year at the end of July Pasteur returned to his father's house, where he reviewed his experimental data and made plans for new studies. In September he attended the International Congress for Hygiene at Geneva, where he intended to read a paper on the attenuation of viruses. He also wished to meet his rival Robert Koch who had criticized his findings. The German professor did not think much of it. "Attenuation of viruses," he had said, "that's too good to be true!"

When Pasteur contradicted his objections, Robert Koch refused to discuss the subject, stating that he would prefer to answer in print. Three months later he published a brochure that was a violent denunciation of Pasteur's work. Pasteur promptly replied in an open letter:

Though accustomed to contradictions of every kind, I must admit that I was perturbed to read in your brochure that in the study of a disease I do not care to look for the microbes and to find out where they are, and that I specifically neglect to prove their parasitic nature. Really, had I not these lines before my eyes, I would not believe that they ever have been written. [The closing words were:] "I am awaiting with confidence the benefits that the attenuation of germs holds in store for the human race in its struggle against the diseases that threaten it.

. . .

Shortly after his return from Geneva, Pasteur, his mind effervescing and his energy seemingly unimpaired by his handicap, decided to go to the department of Vaucluse, where he intended to study swine erysipelas. Outbreaks of this disease caused terrific damage in several countries. In the United States it had carried away over a million hogs in 1879. The infection had also reached epidemic proportions in England and Germany. In France several departments (Côtes-du-Nord, Le Poitou, and those of the Rhône valley) were affected. Pasteur's collaborator Thuillier had discovered the germ of the disease a few months earlier, so there was hope of achieving immunization against the pest.

Pasteur arrived on November 15 in Bollène with Thuillier and a young laboratory technician, Adrien Loir. Town and countryside were reeking with dead or dying hogs. "It reminds me," wrote Pasteur to his wife, "of the silkworm disease. The pigstys with their sick or dead animals take the place of the nurseries stricken with pébrine. At least 20,000 animals are dead, and the scourge is even more prevalent in the Ardèche region."

A short while after his arrival Pasteur learned to his surprise that in that area the breeding of rabbits and pigeons had been abandoned because these species were subject to fatal epizootic diseases. He suspected that there was a connection between these and swine erysipelas. The experiment soon gave proof that actually rabbits and pigeons were susceptible to swine erysipelas. The next step was to investigate whether the virulence of the erysipelas microbe would be modified by passing it through rabbits and pigeons. Pasteur and Thuillier observed that the germ when passing through the organism of a pigeon increased in virulence. On the other hand, passage through rabbits attenuated the virulence to the point of conferring immunity to hogs. This important discovery confirmed Pasteur's previous observations in the case of chicken cholera and anthrax, where the virulence of the germs had been modified by passages through different animals. The practical result was a successful method of vaccination against swine erysipelas.

The beginning of the year 1883 was marked by violent attacks by a clinician, Michel Peter, Professor at the Medical Faculty of Paris, against the Pasteurian doctrines. "What do I, as a medical man," he declared, "care about the mind of a chemist, physicist, or physiologist? I am not interested in your microbes!"

For several months Pasteur had not attended the meetings of the Academy of Medicine; he was disgusted with the unsubstantiated charges, which were in the name of traditional medicine, made against the germ theory. He could not let Peter's diatribe go unanswered, however. With his usual vehemence, he turned to his adversary: "M. Peter ought to make a scrupulous investigation of the subject he is talking about, and, before all, let time do its job. The history of the violent opposition to Jenner's vaccine, in the first years of its application, should serve him as warning against premature judgment."

In the month of August, 1883, Pasteur sent a mission to Egypt consisting of his co-workers Roux and Thuillier and an assistant professor of the Paris Medical Faculty, Straus. The objective was an investigation of the cholera epidemic that was raging in Egypt. Thuillier was stricken with the disease he wanted to fight, and died in Alexandria on September 18. Pasteur felt greatly depressed: "I can only console myself with this loss," he wrote, "by thinking of what he has done for our beloved country."

XXXI

IN spite of personal preoccupations and problems Pasteur went ahead with his researches on rabies. At an age where in most men the spirit of invention is waning, he gave proof of an amazing imagination that was, however, always restrained by the most rigid experimental control.

Since the beginning of 1882, when he had established a reliable method of transmitting hydrophobia by inoculating spinal material of a mad dog to the brain surface of a trepaned dog, he had wondered whether the virulence of the rabies virus could be attenuated. And how was this to be done when the microbe was invisible? Again and again he tried with Emile Roux to solve this perplexing problem. They found the solution.

On May 19, 1884, at the Academy of Sciences Pasteur, together with Chamberland and Roux, made a sensational report. The salient points were these: By passing from dog to monkey, and eventually from monkey to monkey, the virulence of the rabies virus is gradually weakened. After repeated passages through monkeys, the virus, when now transmitted to dogs, rabbits, and guinea pigs, remains attenuated. Then, by passages through rabbits, it becomes rekindled, but several transfers are needed to restore the virus to its maximal potency.

In this way, he had at his disposal viruses of varying strength. It had become possible to make a dog resistant to hydrophobia. All one had to do was to inoculate the dog with spinal material from an infected rabbit, containing highly attenuated virus, and subsequently using a stronger and stronger one. "In view of the long incubation period of rabies," explained Pasteur, "I feel justified in the belief that one can certainly achieve immunity in persons who have been bitten before the fatal disease breaks out."

He asked that a commission be called to substantiate his findings. With the same confidence he had exhibited prior to his experiments in Pouilly-le-Fort, he outlined to the commission his program and the results to be expected:

> The key experiment, [he wrote] would consist in taking from my kennels 20 dogs immune to hydrophobia, to be compared with 20 control animals. We would let these 40 dogs one after another be bitten by rabid dogs. If my statements are correct, all the 20 dogs I consider immune, will resist rabies while the 20 controls will contract it. A second experiment, no less decisive, would use a series of 40 dogs, 20 vaccinated, 20 unvaccinated; they will be trepaned and inoculated at the surface of the brain with the rabies material. The first 20 dogs will resist the infection, the others will all succumb to rabies, either paralyzed or maddened.

What audacity! To Pasteur's mind, here as in the immunization against anthrax, the experiments had to be 100 per cent successful! Never had a biologist delivered such a challenge. The commission started out by appropriating funds for a large isolated kennel yard, needed to accommodate scores of animals. A suitable site was found near Paris, in the park of Villeneuve l'Etang, and the experiments proceeded. The results were, as members of the commission agreed, magnificent, awarding the highest honor to French science and to M. Pasteur another claim on the gratitude of mankind. Nevertheless, Pasteur did not consider the rabies problem solved, and he kept pursuing his researches. In a letter of May 29 to her son and her son-in-law Mme Pasteur reported: "Your father, always very busy, talks little, sleeps little, in other words, continues the life that I started with him 35 years ago."

In August 1884 an International Congress of Medicine took place at Copenhagen. Pasteur represented France. He had hardly arrived at the capital when he was taken on an excursion to Carlsberg, to visit a large brewery that had adopted his methods. At the end of the street leading to the brewery and named after him, Pasteur had the satisfaction of seeing his own statue, created by the famous French sculptor Paul Dubois.

During one of the major sessions of the congress, Pasteur gave a summary of his studies on hydrophobia. He emphasized the point that, although the germ of the disease had neither been seen or cultivated, an attenuated virus could be obtained. And logically he concluded: "The important scientific fact is that it is definitely possible to devise a vaccination against a contagious disease without getting hold of the microbe, without being able to isolate and cultivate it."

How prophetic were these words! Indeed, Pasteur's researches on rabies laid the groundwork to subsequent investigations of those infections where the causative agent cannot be traced with an ordinary microscope, diseases that are nowadays called virus or viral diseases. Actually, rabies is a virus infection of the nervous system, just as smallpox is a virus disease of the skin and mucous membranes. In modern microbiology, the term virus applies to a class of pathogenic as well as saprophytic micro-organisms that can only be seen with an electron microscope, pass the finest pores of porcelain filters, and require special culture media, containing living tissues, for their development. When pathogenic, they are often transmitted by insects and infested material and prey on plants, animals, and man, invading particular organs such as the skin, nervous system, lungs, liver, or causing a generalized infection such as measles, dengue fever, and typhus.

Pasteur's communication was hailed by an enthusiastic public. Never had an experimental method achieved such wonderful feats, and yet Pasteur was well on his way to accomplish even more.

The process of vaccination against rabies by means of virus weakened by animal passages was too complicated. A simpler technique was needed. Pasteur had noted that the virus, in the course of successive passages, acquired a certain fixation, typical of the species in question. He inoculated, after trepanation, material from the spinal cord of a rabid rabbit to another rabbit, from this to a third, and so on. After the twenty-first passage rabies manifested itself after eight days. Continuing the passages, he arrived at an incubation period of seven days; from this moment on the incubation time remained constant: this was a virus of *fixed* virulence.

Looking farther ahead, Pasteur wondered whether the spinal cord of a rabid rabbit, taken from the animal, might serve as a natural culture medium for the virus wherein its virulence could be attenuated gradually. This was analogous to his experience with aged cultures of chicken cholera and anthrax germs. So he dissected the spinal cord of an infected animal and exposed it to air dried by potassium particles deposited at the bottom of the container. The virulence decreased slowly to zero. By daily implantations under the skin of weakened spinal material, he succeeded in making a dog immune to hydrophobia. He started by using a two-week-old spinal cord, then gradually more and more recent material, finally one-day-old spinal material. This done, he could inoculate a dog with highly potent rabies virus under the skin or even at the surface of the brain; no rabies appeared.

A working method of vaccination was established. Because rabies in dogs has an incubation period of several weeks, it sufficed to give a series of injections promptly after the bite, and the animal was saved. Pasteur's admirable capacity for reasoning and experimentation had led to this milestone in immunology. To be sure, there are nowadays other procedures for obtaining an antirabies vaccine. However, Pasteur's method remains original in its principles and effective in its application. Until recent years it was standard procedure at the Pasteur Institute.

XXXII

PASTEUR and his associate Emile Roux lived at the Ecole Normale in the rue d'Ulm. They were absorbed in their work. Pasteur was always the first to arrive at the laboratory. "Every morning at eight," said Roux, "I could hear his hasty and somewhat dragging step, rattling a loose paving stone under the window of my room." As soon as he had entered the laboratory, Pasteur took a pencil and a piece of cardboard; he inspected the cultures in the incubator, then he went to the basement to look at the animals. He made notes in his fine handwriting, not neglecting any detail. Finally, he had Chamberland and Roux give the injections to the animals, as his contracted left hand hindered him in holding tubes and bulbs to fill the syringes. Then they proceeded to the autopsies of the dead animals, to inoculate the culture tubes, and to examine the specimens under the microscope. "One must have seen Pasteur at his microscope to get an idea of the patience with which he used to examine a specimen. What's more, he regarded everything with the same exacting diligence; nothing escaped his shortsighted eyes," said Roux.

After entering in his notebook each of his observations, Pasteur decided on the experiments to be undertaken during the day. Sometimes master and disciples did not agree, but Pasteur was always open to suggestions and discussions; "one could freely express his thoughts," said Dr. Roux, "never have I heard him object to a good argument."

At half past eleven Mme Pasteur called her husband for lunch. When he was obsessed by an idea for a new experiment, he remained silent, and his wife respected his meditation. After the usually frugal meal he returned to the laboratory. At a quarter past one, Mme Pasteur came to tell him that it was time to see his son-in-law, René Vallery-Radot, who would escort him to this or that academy or conference. They got into a rented carriage, a shabby battered coupe, drawn by an asthmatic horse; the driver in livery wore a polished high hat that would look ridiculous nowadays.

Vallery-Radot used to take care of his father-in-law until the end of the day, leaving him unattended only during the sessions in which he was not allowed to take part. At five in the afternoon Pasteur returned to the rue d'Ulm. Carefully he registered in his memorandum book the notes of his collaborators and checked their reports, for he trusted only his own observations; as he used to say: "I must see with my own eyes." To Chamberland and Roux he gave an abstract of the scientific observations that he had just heard and of the discussions that he had presented. At times he gave vent to his indignation; "I wouldn't be at all surprised," he exclaimed one day, "if that unreasonable fellow beats his wife!"

His enthusiasm was overpowering. He suggested the most amazing experimental schemes, evolving from an imagination sometimes disturbing in its audacity. "Ah, wouldn't it be wonderful if we were successful in that!" he said to his assistants on many occasions. It is all the more remarkable that a man with such power of imagination was at the same time endowed with absolute rigidity in experimenting and with an imperturbable logic. It is because these cardinal qualities were inseparably fused in his character that he accomplished his prodigious work.

In the evening, after dinner, he often dictated to his wife a note for the Academy of Sciences. He used to keep it for days and weeks, revising it incessantly, discussing it with Chamberland and Roux. When it seemed faultless, Mme Pasteur copied the manuscript in her perfect handwriting for publication. Thus family life and scientific life were interwoven in Pasteur's household.

XXXIII

ON March 28, 1885, Pasteur wrote to his friend Jules Vercel: "I have demonstrated this year that one can vaccinate dogs or render them immune to rabies after they have been bitten by mad dogs. I have not yet dared to treat humans bitten by rabid dogs. But this moment is not far off, and I seriously think of starting with myself, which means to inoculate myself with rabies and then arrest its effect; so hardened have I become and so sure of my results."

In the beginning of July he had accumulated 50 dogs of all ages and types which he had made resistant to hydrophobia, without a single failure. Then fate took a hand. On Monday the sixth, three unexpected visitors from Alsace entered his laboratory. One was Théodore Vone, a grocer from Meissengott near Schlestadt, who had been bitten at the arm on July 4 by his dog, which had developed rabies; the second was nine-year-old Joseph Meister, who had been bitten at 8.00 A.M. of that day by the same dog. The boy had been thrown to the ground by the mad animal and showed numerous cruel wounds on hands, thighs, and lower legs. The third person—who had not been bitten—was the boy's mother. At the autopsy of the dog, shot dead by his owner, the stomach had been found filled with hay, straw, and pieces of wood, characteristic of a rabid dog.

The man Vone had been bitten through the shirt which had caught the dog's teeth, the skin being intact. He had nothing to fear, and Pasteur assured him that he could return home the same day. But what about the hapless child? Leaving him without treatment would mean an almost certain death sentence; treating him with the vaccine would mean a terrible risk. However effective the vaccine was in dogs, who could tell whether it would work as well in man and whether it might kill the boy? It was a dramatic decision to make, and Pasteur hesitated.

That evening, the weekly session of the Academy of Sciences took place. Pasteur confided his doubts to Dr. Vulpian and Dr. Grancher, who came to examine little Joseph and noted that he had fourteen wounds. From the number and severity of the injuries they came to the conclusion that the prognosis was extremely grave. In view of such precarious circumstances Pasteur decided, "not without acute and cruel anxiety," to try out on Joseph Meister the method that had invariably proven successful in dogs.

At 8.00 P.M.—sixty hours after being bitten on July 4—the boy was inoculated under the skin of the abdomen, with a small portion of spinal cord removed from a rabbit two weeks before, thus containing attenuated virus. Pasteur had Dr. Grancher give this, as well as the subsequent injections, for two reasons; his left hand being paralyzed, it would have been difficult for him, and, above all, not being a physician, he had no legal right to administer treatments. From July 7 to July 13 inoculations were made daily or even twice a day, with more and more recent material. The injection on July 13 was made with four-day-old spinal cord.

On that day, Mme Pasteur wrote to her daughter and to her son-in-law: "My dear children, another bad night for your father. He cannot make up his mind to use the last resort on this child. And yet it has to be done now." The last resort meant the test injections with the most virulent rabies material.

The same day, Pasteur expressed himself in a letter to his son-in-law: "Dear René, I believe that great things are in the offing. Joseph Meister has left the laboratory. He feels very well this morning, he has slept well though a bit restless, has good appetite, and no temperature." At the end of his letter, anxious and yet hopeful for the imminent victory that his wife predicted in her common sense and optimism, he invited his son-in-law to spend two or three days at the Ecole Normale: "One of the great medical events of the century is in progress, and you would regret missing it."

The last injections, which caused Pasteur grave misgivings, were made on July 14, 15, and 16, with three-day-, then two-day-, and finally one-day-old spinal cord. On the evening of this fateful trial little Meister went to sleep peacefully. Pasteur spent a night of torment. Only his wife had no doubts about the outcome.

The treatment of the youngster being completed, Pasteur, worn out by the emotional tension, agreed to take a few days' rest at Marrault near Avallon (Yonne) on the estate of his son-in-law. But he was haunted by thoughts of the child. Every morning he waited nervously for a letter or telegram from Dr. Grancher, who took care of the boy and kept Pasteur informed. At the end of July he left for Arbois, still pursued by nightmares, as he wrote to Dr. Grancher.

On July 27, when Meister was supposed to return to Alsace, Pasteur sent a letter to Dr. Weber, the country doctor who had first attended the boy when he was bitten. He asked him to give the boy stamped envelopes so that he could write to him at least every other day, and closed with these words: "My apprehension is extreme." However, when the days went by, Pasteur calmed down. September and October passed in the certainty of success. And on October 25, at the Academy of Sciences, Pasteur made the famous report on his "Method of Preventing Rabies After a Bite." "After I might say innumerable experiments," he announced, "I have arrived at a prophylactic method, practical and prompt, the success of which has been so convincing in dogs, that I have confidence in its general application in all animals and even in man." He described the treatment course to which he had subjected the Meister boy and finished: "To-day, three months and three weeks after the accident, his health leaves nothing to be desired."

This spectacular achievement had tremendous repercussions in the scientific world as well as among the public. People who had been bitten by mad dogs started to pour into Pasteur's laboratory. Inoculations were made every morning at eleven. Pasteur himself called out the names of the patients. "He took a personal interest in every case," wrote René Vallery-Radot; "when he heard of a poor peasant arriving in the big city, he arranged to put him up at a neighborhood hotel, and made things easy for him. Above all, he was concerned about children."

On November 9, a girl of ten, Louise Pelletier, was admitted, 37 days after she had been severely bitten on the head by a mountain dog. This was a desperate case; actually, it was too late for even a remote chance of an effective preventive treatment. In scientific fairness to his methods, Pasteur should have refused to treat the doomed child. If she died, as was almost certain, it would unduly alarm all those trusting people who had already been treated and might discourage others from seeking protection. On the other hand, it would be cruel not to try to save the unfortunate victim whose parents had come with hopeful hearts. So Pasteur decided, although certain of failure, to have Louise treated with his vaccine.

The inoculations went on without mishap, but when the treatment was ended, the child had difficulty in breathing and was seized with convulsions; she could not take fluids any more. Pasteur went to see her immediately; new injections were tried. On December 2 Pasteur spent a whole day at the girl's bedside in the little apartment in the rue Dauphine where the Pelletier family was staying. He could not part from the child who, gasping for breath, implored him not to leave her. When all hope was gone, he burst into tears.

Fifteen years later, the father of Louise, after reading René Vallery-Radot's *Life of Pasteur*, wrote to him: "Of all great men whose lives I have known, Pasteur seems to me the greatest. I never met a single one who would have done what he did in the case of my little daughter—sacrifice long years of toil as a scientist, jeopardize a universal reputation, and deliberately embark upon a dismal failure, for the sake of humanity."

A few days after the death of little Louise, Pasteur received a cable from New York, announcing that four little Americans, children of workmen's families, were on their way to Paris. They had been bitten by mad dogs, and the *New York Herald* had raised the funds for their voyage by an appeal to the public. The children arrived at Pasteur's laboratory, accompanied by a doctor and the mother of the youngest, a five-year-old boy. This one asked, after getting his first inoculation: "And for that we had to make such a long journey?" When the youngsters returned safe and sound to New York, a crowd was milling around on the pier to greet them and to deluge them with questions about the scientist "who performed miracles."

Amidst his laborious work, Pasteur found time to write to the children whom he had vaccinated against hydrophobia. He inquired about their education and offered them advice.

Why don't you let me hear from you as you promised? [he asked in a letter] Maybe it's because you don't know how to read and write. In that case you should make every effort to learn. If you need money to have leisure time and to pay for instruction, let me know. Tell me about your family. Have you a father and a mother? Have you brothers or sisters? If you cannot write to me, have my questions answered by your mayor, your teacher, or your priest.

Pasteur was beloved by everyone. The confidence he inspired and the affection he earned were indubitably the reflection of the genuine interest and sympathy he extended to the people who came to him as to a savior from all parts of France and from foreign lands. "I carry him in my heart, the little boy [Joseph Meister] who for long weeks has been to me a source of worry," he wrote to the editor of the *Journal d'Alsace*.

On March 1, 1886, Pasteur submitted to the Academy of Sciences his statistics on those who had been treated with antirabies vaccinations. Out of 350, one fatality: the Pelletier girl. He could state that "the prophylaxis of rabies after bites has been established." Now he recommended setting up an organization for antirabic vaccination. A commission, appointed by the Academy of Sciences, unanimously adopted this project, to be named the Pasteur Institute. An international subscription was opened, and the response was gratifying indeed. From almost every country donations came in, piling up into millions of francs for the construction of a model laboratory in the rue Dutot. It was to be a fitting monument to the master, to serve not only as a treatment center for antirabies therapy but also as a focus of continued and expanded scientific research.

XXXIV

FROM all over the world physicians and scientists flocked to Paris to familiarize themselves with the method of prophylactic treatment against rabies and with the Pasteurian doctrines, which had revolutionized medical science. From New York, where an antirabic institute was planned, Dr. Valentine Mott was sent to obtain the vaccine and instructions. Amidst the general enthusiasm a gala performance for the benefit of the new establishment was held at the Trocadéro Palace. Pasteur felt somewhat out of place among the celebrities of the entertainment world, the actors who recited excerpts from plays, and the musicians who performed works by Gounod, Massenet, and Saint-Saëns. At a banquet in the evening he said: "You have come, great artists and great actors, to lend your support to those who want to serve suffering mankind. Should I dare confess that I hear practically all of you for the first time? I don't think I have spent more than ten evenings at the theater in my whole life."

There were not only devoted followers, however. Certain doctors and certain journalists, always on the alert for something that might erupt into a scandal, pursued Pasteur with their attacks. The death of little

Louise Pelletier and that of 3 Russians out of 19 who had come from the province of Smolensk to undergo antirabies treatment, unleashed a vicious smear campaign. Pasteur, it was charged, did not prevent rabies—he gave it! The public was invited to Antipasteurian Meetings with topics such as "The Alleged Discoveries of M. Pasteur," his "heresies" and "frauds." The *Ami du Peuple* ranted: "The discoveries by Pasteur are nothing but a hoax, grafted upon the boldest lies. He cures rabies no more than the silkworms. . . . He is lying, as he has lied brazenly in all his scientific reports for the past ten years." In the *Union libérale* Pasteur was maligned as a "deluded individual, a degraded chemist, an object of ridicule, whose frustrations should teach a lesson to those phony scientists who meddle into subjects they don't understand."

Every day Pasteur received anonymous letters, every day appeared vilifying articles. He was accused of homicide. Insidious pamphlets denouncing the laboratory at the Ecole Normale were distributed in the streets of Paris. "I never knew I had so many enemies," said Pasteur sadly. He could not stand so many calumnies. Thoughts of the anguish brought on in people who had already undergone antirabic treatment obsessed him. His health began to falter. In November 1886 he developed symptoms of coronary insufficiency. He had to take a rest at the Italian Riviera, in

Bordighera, where one of his admirers put a villa at his disposal.

On January 4, 1887, a violent attack on the anti-rabies vaccination was made at the Academy of Medicine by Professor Peter on the occasion of a fatality following vaccination of a child. He declared the method dangerous and lethal instead of protective. In the following months Peter continued his charges, which were the more insidious as Pasteur was not there to deal with his adversary. In his absence the physicians Grancher, Dujardin-Beaumetz, and Brouardel had to bear the brunt of the controversy. Professor Vulpian, shocked by Peter's tactics, retorted: "How can one help being dismayed by such accusations, hurled against a man like M. Pasteur, whose good faith, loyalty, and scientific integrity may serve as a model to his foes and friends alike? Never has M. Pasteur lost sight of the darker side of the method he created. Every time he has published his statistics, he has cited the rare cases where his treatment has not succeeded."

In the midst of these nerve-wracking troubles a dramatic event occurred. On Ash Wednesday, February 23, at half past six in the morning, a violent earthquake shook the villa where Pasteur stayed with his family. As Mme Pasteur wrote to her son: "there was a terrible cracking and rocking of the entire house." In a minute it was over. The children, Camille and Louis, "more dead than alive," ran to their grandparents' room. Then came another terrifying wave. Mme Pasteur was petrified, her husband in a state of extreme excitement. One of the columns of the clock tower was shattered, the cracked ceilings were coming down, and the rest of the splintering house seemed to stand up only by a miracle.

At three in the afternoon Pasteur left Bordighera with his wife, his daughter, his son-in-law, and his grandchildren. They could not proceed to Menton before 11.00 P.M. because all trains were delayed. Between Geneva and Cannes throngs of travelers, panic-sticken by the earthquake, which had ravaged the whole region, stormed the railroad stations to flee from Italy to France or from France to Italy. Pasteur went to Arbois and stayed there for several weeks.

On May 10, 1887, he returned to Paris to take part in a session of the Academy of Medicine. On July 5 he deposited at the office of the Academy the copy of a report made by an English commission in which Sir James Paget and Joseph Lister were participants. This commission had come to Paris to study the method of vaccination against rabies. "In my long scientific career," said Pasteur in presenting the report, "I have never experienced such joy as when I read this." He felt the report compensated for all the base insults and the slander he had endured. Peter tried to reopen the discussions. Pasteur replied disdainfully:

"As to the question of a prolonged discussion with the individual who just has spoken, I refuse to agree to that, for I find this individual, and I am ready to prove it, totally incompetent in clinical and experimental matters."

Peter, however, did not lay down arms. On July 12 he became even more abusive in the absence of Pasteur. Dr. Brouardel repudiated all his objections, statistically and otherwise. "It comes as a painful surprise to me," he said, "that we hear accusations from this platform against a man who for thirty years has made so many brilliant and valuable discoveries."

The great neurologist Charcot exclaimed, full of respect and admiration for Pasteur: "Yes, I am convinced I am in accord with every unbiased and open-minded physician who has been concerned with this problem when I say that the inventor of the antirabic vaccination can, now more than ever, hold his head high in pursuing his glorious task, undisturbed by the clamor of back-biters and the whisperings of jealous detractors."

XXXV

A FEW months later, Pasteur made his triumphant entry into the Institute that bears his name. It was dedicated on November 14, 1888. "Alas," said Pasteur in his oration, "mine is the poignant melancholy of entering it as a man 'vanquished by Time!'" These closing words, timely as ever, have often been quoted:

Two laws seem to be in conflict today, a law of blood and death which, devising new arms every day, forces the nations to be always ready for war, and a law of peace, work, and salvation, solely geared to deliver mankind from the scourges besetting it. One aims at violent conquest, the other at the welfare of humanity. One extols Life above all victories, the other would sacrifice hundreds of thousands of human beings for the ambition of a single one. Which of these laws will prevail? Only God knows.

At his Institute, which became a teaching and research center for the study of infectious diseases and soon had branches in many countries, Pasteur saw the science he had founded develop and bear fruit. Outstanding discoveries were made constantly. Chamberland and Roux demonstrated that immunization could be effected by means of heat-killed bacteria; this is the method employed today for protection against a score of contagious diseases. Of enormous consequence was the discovery by Roux and Yersin that the filtrate of cultures of diphtheria bacilli contains an exceedingly powerful toxin, responsible for the dangerous course of the infection. This led to the discovery of antitoxins by Behring in Germany, revolutionizing the treatment of diphtheria. Roux then established the serotherapy of tetanus, Calmette the serotherapy against snake bites. Later Calmette and Alphonse Guérin introduced the BCG vaccine for the prevention of tuberculosis, a potent weapon in the fight against the "white plague." The Russian-born biologist Metchnikoff established his theory of phagocytosis, demonstrating that bacteria are ingested and destroyed by certain white blood cells (phagocytes), a defense mechanism against infection. He also worked with Roux on syphilis. Jules Bordet together with Octave Gengou (who later discovered the bacillus of whooping cough) discovered certain antibodies in blood serum, leading to valuable diagnostic tests.

Pasteur had no strength left for work but his spirit kept stimulating his disciples—who were called Pasteurians. "The only consolation, when we feel our own power decline," he used to say, "is to be aware that we can help those who come after us to do more and better work than ours, marching on with their eyes fixed to the great horizons that we have only glimpsed."

Pasteur's apartment was adjacent to the laboratory. Mme Pasteur was very friendly with the researchers, took interest in their work, and was always solicitous toward them and their kin; as Dr. Roux wrote: "she gave the impression that the Institute was one large family." Frenchmen, Belgians, Swiss, Russians worked there side by side under the aegis of a man whom they regarded as a demigod.

On December 27, 1892, Pasteur celebrated his seventieth birthday. A grandiose ovation was staged at the Sorbonne. Representatives of the academies, the universities, and the scientific societies of France and from abroad paid tribute to him. The great Lister, speaking in the name of all physicians and surgeons, remarked that "Pasteur had lifted the veil that for centuries had hidden the infectious diseases." When Pasteur got up to embrace Lister, there was thundering applause in the huge amphitheater. All delegates then presented to Pasteur the citations they had come to deliver. Since Pasteur was too moved to give his speech of acknowledgment, his son had to read his words for him:

You delegates of foreign countries who have come a long way to show your sympathy for France, have given me the greatest joy a man can feel who believes that Science and Peace will prevail over Ignorance and War, that the nations will learn to understand each other, not for destruction but for advancement, and that the future belongs to those who have done most for suffering mankind. [Then he called on the younger generation:] Young men . . . live in the serene peace of the laboratories and libraries. Ask yourselves first: What have I done for my education? And as you gradually advance: What have I done for my country?—until the moment comes when you experience the tremendous gratification of knowing that in some measure you have contributed to the progress and welfare of mankind. More or less favored by the current of life as your efforts may be, you must have the right to say, on approaching the great goal: I have done all I could do.

This ceremony was the last act in the public life of Pasteur. From then on he was restricted to his family circle. My parents, my sister, and I [1] lived in his shade. His simplicity and kindness were overwhelming. When you approached him, you were struck by the penetrating yet gentle gaze of his gray-green eyes. His will power was expressed in a high and large forehead; his figure appeared to be hewn from a block of granite. His left forearm was bent permanently, completely contracted; the fingers of his left hand were flexed and immobile, except for the thumb.

On some mornings when I visited him at his home in the Institute, he took me to the "Rabies Service."

[1] Pasteur was survived by his son Jean-Baptiste (1851–1908), who was in the Foreign Office, and his daughter Marie-Louise, who married René Vallery-Radot. She had three children: Marie-Madeleine, who died as an infant; Camille (1880–1927); and Pasteur Vallery-Radot, born in 1886, author of this book.

There were always dozens of "bitten persons" waiting in the anteroom. Pasteur leaned on a wooden desk, behind the doctor who gave the injections, watching in silence. When the needle entered the skin with difficulty, he made a gesture of suffering, so distressing was the pain of a fellow man to him. Among the children he distributed fine new sous that he always kept handy for this purpose.

My parents resided in an old, austere, and gloomy building at 14, rue de Grenelle. Pasteur came to visit us every day at half past one. Painfully he climbed the two stairs leading to our apartment. When he arrived at my father's studio, he would take my sister and me on his knees. About two o'clock he took a few steps on the rather deserted terrace of the Tuileries, leaning on my father's arm, walking with difficulty because of his lame left leg. After this brief promenade he would attend an academy or a conference.

Pasteur's love and affection for his grandchildren were apparent at all times. There is, among many other letters, a note he wrote to his granddaughter on her birthday:

When you receive these few lines tomorrow, the tenth year of your life will be completed. I am quite dreamy and really touched, full of emotion that makes me cry. During these ten years, I believe, I never thought of you without loving you more and more, always convinced that some day you will become an accomplished young lady. You will not fail, I am sure, during the ten new years that start tomorrow. Quick now, promise me that!

And on one of his speeches I found this dedication:

To my dear grandson. When you are grown up, I shall not be here any more; but at least I'll carry with me, in my hopeful heart, the memory of you and your little sister in the cradle, of your smile and of your look which always charmed me and which, I hope, will for a long time to come delight your good grandmothers and your dear parents.

Summers were spent in the vicinity of Paris, at Villeneuve l'Etang, where the government had provided an estate for Pasteur's experiments on hydrophobia. There was a very modest dwelling which, in former times, had served as an outbuilding to the Castle. Pasteur's room had a monastic appearance. In the neighborhood were rabbits' cages, kennels, and vast stables for horses from which blood was withdrawn for serotherapy.

In September we used to go to Arbois. I still can see my grandfather in his studio, overlooking the river Cuisance. I see him before me, again walking on the road to Besançon, surrounded by his wife, his daughter, his son-in-law, and his grandchildren. Leaning on one of us, he climbed painfully the ridge leading to the vineyard where in 1878 he had made his famous experiments on the fermentation of wine. He liked to reminisce about his childhood and experiences in his life; he spoke with affection of his parents and of his sisters who were buried in the town. Sometimes a farmer accosted him, calling him informally by his first name; it was a former classmate. Pasteur stopped and talked to him kindly; then he continued his walk. Who would have guessed that this plain man was the great scientist whom the entire world worshipped?

Pasteur's health was undermined by a life overcharged with ideas, emotions, work, and struggles. On November 23, 1887, nineteen years after the first stroke, which had left him half paralyzed, he had had another cerebral hemorrhage, which affected his speech. On November 1, 1894, he suffered his third stroke. After this fateful November day he did not leave his room any more. He never complained lest he would upset his dear ones. The chiefs of the department of the Institute took turns in attending him. Mme Pasteur stayed constantly close to his bed, anxiously watching the rhythm of his breathing when he fell asleep.

In June 1895 he went to Villeneuve l'Etang for the last time. His strength ebbed away day by day. In the afternoons he was taken in an armchair into the shade of the purple beech trees in the park, where he received the research workers of the Institute and some intimate friends. On September 28, 1895, the end came. From hour to hour the light of his eyes and the radiance of his mind were waning. At 4:45 in the afternoon, one hand in his wife's hand, the other holding a crucifix, he died.

The next day, the sun rose as always; the human anthill continued its futile agitation; nothing seemed changed on the face of the earth—but the man who, like few before him, had enriched and ennobled the human race, who had proven with unflagging enthusiasm what a mortal can accomplish, was gone. The world had lost in value.

Pasteur's last will, which was found after his death, was typical of his simplicity: "This is my testament: I leave to my wife all that the law permits me to leave to her. May my children never stray from the path of duty and always bestow upon their mother the affection she deserves."

The government arranged an imposing state funeral for its great son. Flanked by a reverent and silent crowd, which formed a double file in honor of the man who had done so much to allay human suffering, the cortege proceeded from the Pasteur Institute to Notre Dame Cathedral.

Pasteur was buried in a marble crypt, erected in his memory by his wife and children. At the entrance one reads this inscription of his words:

Blessed is the Man who Carries in his Soul a God, a Beautiful Ideal that he Obeys—Ideal of Art, Ideal of Science, Ideal of the Fatherland, Ideal of the Virtues of the Gospel.

The mosaics adorning the crypt represent allegories alluding to Pasteur's work. On marble plaques—like victories on war monuments—his principal discoveries are engraved:

Molecular Asymmetry/Fermentations/Spontaneous Generation/Studies on Wine/Diseases of Silkworms/Studies on Beer/Virulent Diseases/Virus—Vaccines/Prophylaxis of Rabies

In front of an altar the body of Mme Pasteur is interred. Her epitaph reads:

Here rests Marie Pasteur.
Socia rei humanæ atque divinæ.

SOURCES

Oeuvres de Pasteur, Réunies par Pasteur Vallery-Radot. Paris: Masson & Cie; 1933–9. 7 vol.

Correspondence de Pasteur, Réunie et annotée par Pasteur Vallery-Radot. Paris: Flammarion. 4 vol.

Dubos, René J.: *Louis Pasteur, Free Lance of Science.* 418 p. Boston: Little, Brown & Co.

Duclaux, Emile: *Histoire d'un esprit.* 400 p. Paris: Masson & Cie.

Vallery-Radot, Pasteur: *Pasteur inconnu.* 248 p. Paris: Flammarion.

Vallery-Radot, René: *La Vie de Pasteur.* 733 p. Paris: Flammarion. (American Edition, translated by Mrs. R. L. Devonshire: *The Life of Pasteur.* 484 p. New York: Doubleday, Page & Co.; 1920.)

Vallery-Radot, René: *Madame Pasteur.* 157 p. Paris: Flammarion.

❀ i ❀

INDEX

Académie Française, 38, 157–60
Academy of Medicine, 123, 124, 125, 128, 133, 134, 137, 140, 141, 146–7, 186, 187
Academy of Sciences, 27, 32, 34, 37, 54, 55, 56, 65, 66, 69, 70, 73, 84–5, 106, 107, 125, 128, 167, 175, 177, 179, 183
"aerobia" and "anaerobia," 70, 74, 133
Agricultural Society, Melun, 148–9, 150
Alès, 88, 89, 90, 92, 97, 101, 108, 110
Alfort, 133
Ami du Peuple, 185
Ampère, Marie, 45
Andral, Gabriel, 106
anthrax, 130–5, 147–52, 161–2, 165, 169, 171
Antipasteurian Meetings, 185
antiseptic method, 124–5, 140–1
Arago, François, 34, 35
Arbois, 10, 11, 13, 14, 15, 16, 17, 32, 57, 81, 83, 89, 92, 115, 134, 144, 179, 194
attenuation of viruses, 163–6, 167–9, 170–2
autoclave, 67
Balard, Antoine Jérôme, 26, 34, 69, 106
Barbet, M., 14, 21, 22, 23, 24
Bastian, M., 67
BCG vaccine, 190
beer, studies on, 119–22, 123, 169, 197
Behring, Emil von, 190
Bernard, Claude, 69, 136, 138
Bert, Paul, 126, 131
Berthelot, Pierre Eugène Marcelin, 136
Bertrand, Joseph, 160
Berzelius, Baron Jöns Jakob, 50
Besançon, 6, 8, 13, 16, 17, 89, 194
Bigo, M., 50
Bimard, Marquis de, 104
Biot, Jean-Baptiste, 34, 37, 48, 55, 61
Blanc, Mont, 64
Boissier, Gaston, 157
Bollène, 164
Bonapartists, 5, 6
Bonn University, 115
Bordeaux, 154–5
Bordet, Jules, 190
Bordighera, 185–6, 187
Bossuet, Jacques Benigne, 62, 160
Bourbaki, Charles Denis Sauter, 116, 117

Breithaupt, Johann August Friedrich, 42
Broglie, Jacques Victor Albert, Duc de, 157
Brouardel, Paul, 186, 188
brucellosis (Malta fever), 85
Brussels, 41
Buffon, Georges Louis Leclerc, Comte de, 59
"bunch of grapes" (staphylococcus), 139

Cagniard de la Tour, Charles, 51
Calmette, Gaston, 190
Cantoni, Carlo, 90–1
Carlsberg brewery, Copenhagen, 169
Caro, Elme Marie, 157
Central Institute, 27
Central Veterinary School, Paris, 161
Chamalières, 119
Chamberland, Charles Edouard, 135, 138, 144–5, 149, 150, 167, 172, 174, 175, 189
Chambéry, 92
Chappuis, M., 21, 26, 36, 40, 53
Charcot, Jean Martin, 188
chicken cholera, 144–5, 165, 171
childbirth fever, *see* puerperal sepsis
cholera, 166; *see also* chicken cholera
Clermont-Ferrand, 119
Colin, Professor, 133–4, 149–50, 151
Collège de France, 34
Cologne, 41
Comte, Auguste, 157
Copenhagen, 169
Cornalia, Emile Balthazar Marie, 90, 91
crystallography, 29, 32, 35, 39–43, 44–7, 52, 71, 197; *see also* fermentations
crystallology, *see* crystallography

Davaine, Casimir Joseph, 130, 131
Dijon, Lyceum of, 36
diphtheria, 190
diseases, *see* virulent diseases
Dôle, 7, 8, 9
Douai, 5
Dresden, 42
Droz, Joseph, 18–19
Dubois, Paul, 169
Duclaux, Emile, 54, 71–2, 81, 92, 93, 108, 117, 119, 128, 136
Dujardin-Beaumetz, Dr., 186
Dumas, Alexandre *fils*, 157, 160
Dumas, Alexandre *père*, 66
Dumas, Jean-Baptiste, 26–8, 34, 40–1, 55, 56, 61, 69, 70, 87–8, 91, 101, 107, 108, 112, 113, 129, 158
Duruy, Victor, 66, 98

Ecole Normale Supérieure, 13, 17, 20, 21, 23, 24, 25,

Ecole Normale Supérieure (*continued*)
26, 29, 31, 33, 37, 53, 54, 75, 91, 93, 97–9, 104, 106, 107, 116, 153, 173, 178, 185
Egypt, 166
Eure department, 5

Faculty of Sciences, Lille, 48, 49, 53
Faculty of Sciences, Lyon, 128
Faculty of Sciences, Paris, 27, 34
Faculty of Sciences, Strasbourg, 36
Falloux, Frédéric Alfred Pierre, Comte de, 157
Faraday, Michael, 45
Favé, Ildephonse, 99
fermentations, 47, 50–2, 55, 58, 61, 69–70, 79–84, 87, 123, 124, 136–7, 197; *see also* beer, wine
Fikentscher, Herr, 41
Filippi, Filippo de, 90
flacherie, *see* silkworm, diseases of
Fortoul, Hippolyte Nicolas Honoré, 48, 54
Franklin, Benjamin, *Memoirs of Physics*, 22
Freiberg, 42
furunculosis, 139

Gard department, 87, 88, 103, 108
Geneva, 117, 163, 164, 187
Gengou, Octave, 190
germ theory, 130–8, 150–2; *see also* virulent diseases
Gernez, Désiré Jean Baptiste, 92, 93, 107, 108
Godélier, Dr., 113
Grancher, Jacques-Joseph, 177–8, 179, 186
Guérin, Alphonse, 190
Guérin, Jules, 146–7

Hanover, 41
Helmont, Jan Baptista van, 58
Hungary, 42
Huxley, Thomas Henry, 118
hydrophobia, *see* rabies

infectious diseases, *see* virulent diseases
Institut Pasteur, *see* Pasteur Institute
Institute for Silk Culture, Montpellier, 129
International Congress for Hygiene, Geneva (1882), 163
International Congress of Medicine, Copenhagen (1884), 169
International Congress of Medicine, London (1861), 153–4
International Congress of Sericulture, Milan (1876), 128–9

Jacquinet, M., 99
Jaillard, M., 132

Japan, 109, 111
Jenner, Edward, 146, 166
Joly, M., 65, 66
Joubert, Jules François, 135
Journal de Paris, 98
Jura, 3, 64, 82, 127

Kestner, M., 40
Koch, Robert, 131, 163

La Beauce, 142
La Bruyère, François de, 160
La Fontaine, Jean de, 160
Lallier, M., 98, 99
Lamartine, Alphonse de, 29
Lannelongue, Dr., 139
Laurent, M., 36, 37, 38
Lavoisier, Antoine Laurent, 69
Leeuwenhoek, Anton van, 51, 59
Legitimists, 5, 6
Leipzig, 41, 42
Leloir, Louis Auguste, 75
Leplat, M., 132
Liebig, Justus von, 50, 51
Life of Pasteur, Réne Vallery-Radot, 181
Lille, 48, 49, 53
Lister, Joseph, 125, 187, 191
Littré, Maximilien Paul Emile, 157
Loir, Adrien, 164
London, 120, 153–4
Lons-le-Saunier, 128
Lyceum of Dijon, 36
Lyon, 117, 129

Magdeburg, 41
Maillot, M., 92, 108, 128–9
Malta fever (brucellosis), 85
Marnoz, 9, 10
Marrault, 179
Maspero, Sir Gaston Camille Charles, 98–9
Matilde, Princess, 66
Meister, Joseph, 176, 177–9, 180, 183
Melun, 148–9, 150
Memoirs of Physics, Benjamin Franklin, 22
Mer-de-Glace, 64, 65
Metchnikoff, Elie, 190
Miege valley, 3
Milan, 116, 128, 129
milk-borne infectious diseases, 85
molecular asymmetry, *see* crystallography
Moniteur scientifique, 84
Montanvert, 64, 65
Mott, Valentine, 184
Munich, 114
Musset, M., 65, 66
Mussy, Guéneau de, 154

Napoleon I, 4, 5, 13 *n*, 25
Napoleon III, 73, 99, 1 110–11
Needham, John Tui ville, 59–60
New York Herald, 181–2
Nisard, Désiré, 99, 157, 158
Nozeroy, 3

Oersted, Hans Christian, 45
osteomyelitis, 139

Paget, Sir James, 153, 187
Paillot, A., 94–5 *n*
paratartrate, *see* crystallography
Paris Observatory, 64
Pasteur, Camille (daughter), 57, 91
Pasteur, Cécile (daughter), 57, 75, 92
Pasteur, Claude-Etienne (grandfather), 3
Pasteur, Emilie (sister), 18, 37
Pasteur, Jean-Baptiste (son), 44, 56–7, 115, 116–17, 169, 187, 191
Pasteur, Jean-Joseph (father), 3–7, 9, 10, 11, 12–14, 16, 24–5, 26, 29, 30–1, 37, 46, 81, 89
Pasteur, Jeanne (daughter), 44, 56, 57
Pasteur, Jeanne-Etiennette Roqui (mother), 7, 12, 32, 37, 89
Pasteur, Joséphine (sister), 18, 26, 37
Pasteur, Louis: birth, 9; childhood, 9–13; death, 195–7; education and degrees received, 11–28, 115–16; election to Académie Française, 157–60; election to Academy of Medicine, 123; election to Academy of Sciences, 70–1; family, 3–14, 18–19, 21, 24–5, 26, 30, 32, 36–9, 44, 56–7, 74, 91–2, 108–9, 174–5, 192, 193–4, 196–7; health, 19, 106–7, 108–9, 110, 185–6, 192, 193, 194, 195–6; honor and recognition, 17, 27, 35, 55, 116, 118, 125, 126, 129, 135, 141, 151, 153–4, 169, 181, 183, 184, 188, 191, 196; interest in fine arts, 12, 16, 75–7; philosophy, 129, 155, 157–60, 189, 190–2; political and patriotic life, 29–31, 115–18, 127–8; scientific disputes, 61–8, 131–5, 149–51, 196–7; scientific method, 89, 91, 104–5, 120, 159–60, 174–5; scientific research and discoveries, *see* anthrax, autoclave, antiseptic method, beer, chicken cholera, crystallography, fermentations, pasteurization, puerperal sepsis, rabies, silkworm, spontaneous generation, swine erysipelas, virulent diseases, virus–vaccines, wine; teaching positions, 17–18, 36, 43–4, 48–50, 53, 75–7, 97–9; travel, 40–3, 44, 64–5, 79, 88–9, 92, 104, 108, 110, 111–14, 119, 120–1, 128–9, 136–7, 142–3,

Pasteur, Louis (*continued*) 148–51, 153, 154–5, 163, 164, 169
Pasteur, Marie Laurent (wife), 36–9, 46, 56–7, 71, 74, 89, 92, 93, 106, 107, 116–17, 150, 152, 154, 169, 174, 175, 178, 186, 187, 191, 194, 195, 196, 197
Pasteur, Marie-Louise (daughter), *see* Vallery-Radot, Marie-Louise Pasteur
Pasteur, Virginie (sister), 18, 37
Pasteur Institute, 183, 189–91, 192–3, 195, 196
Pasteur oven, 67
Pasteurians, 190
pasteurization, 82–6, 104–5; *see also* fermentations
pébrine, *see* silkworm, diseases of
Pelletier, Louise, 180–1, 183, 184–5
Peter, Michel, 165, 166, 186, 187–8
phagocytosis, 190
Philomatic Society, 71
Pisa, University of, 116
Poggiale, M., 125–6
Pont Gisquet, 92, 93, 110
Pontarlier, 116, 117
Positivism, 157–8
Pouchet, Félix Archimède, 61–3, 65–7
Pouilly-le-Fort, 149–51, 168
Poupet, Mont, 64
Prague, 43
puerperal sepsis, 140–1

Quatrefages de Bréau, Jean Louis Armand de, 90
Quesneville, M. de, 84

rabies, 156–7, 167–9, 170–2, 176–83, 185, 186, 187, 188, 192–3, 194, 197
racemic acid, *see* crystallography
Rammelsburg, Karl Friedrich, 71
Rassman, Dr., 43
Raulin, M., 108, 128
Redi, Francesco, 59
Renan, Ernest, 158–9
Roqui, Jeanne-Etiennette, *see* Pasteur, Jeanne-Etiennette Roqui
Rossignol, M., 149
Rouen, 61
Roux, Emile, 39, 86, 131, 138, 141, 142, 144–5, 148, 150, 156, 166, 167, 173, 174, 175, 189, 190, 191
Ruhmkorff, Henrich Daniel, 45

Salins, 3, 5
Sainte-Beuve, Charles Augustin, 97–8
Sainte-Claire Deville, Henri Etienne, 106–7, 110, 112
Sainte Madeleine, Church of, Strasbourg, 39
Saint-Etienne, 97

Saint-Hippolyte-du-Fort, 108, 110
Saint-Louis Lyceum, 23
Sand, George, 66, 98
Senarmont, Henri Hureau de, 34, 61
silkworm, diseases of, 87–91, 92–6, 101–4, 107, 109–14, 129, 132, 197
smallpox, 144, 146, 170
snakebite, serotherapy of, 190
Sorbonne, 66, 126, 191
Spallanzani, Lazzaro, 59–60
splenic fever, *see* anthrax
spontaneous generation, 58–68, 69–70, 124, 197
staphylococcus, 139
stereochemistry, 35, 47; *see also* crystallography
Strasbourg, 36, 38, 39, 43–4, 114
Straus, M., 166
streptococcus, 94 *n*, 140–1
"string of beads" (streptococcus), 94 *n*, 140–1
swine erysipelas, 164–5
syphilis, 190

Tantonville, 119
tartaric acid, *see* crystallography
tetanus, serotherapy of, 190
Thuillier, M., 164–6
Treatise on Heterogenesis, Pouchet, 61
Trieste, 41, 42, 111
Trocadéro Palace, 184
Trousseau Hospital, 139
tuberculosis, 85, 190
Turin, 161
Tyndall, John, 126

Union libérale, 185

vaccination, 149–52, 161–2, 164–5, 168, 170–2
Vaillant, Jean Baptiste Philbert, 111
Vallery-Radot, Camille (granddaughter of Louis Pasteur), 186–7, 192, 193–4
Vallery-Radot, Marie-Louise Pasteur (daughter), 57, 93, 97, 102, 109, 112–13, 116–17, 178, 187, 192, 194
Vallery-Radot, Marie-Madeleine (granddaughter), 192 *n*
Vallery-Radot, Pasteur (grandson), 186–7, 192, 193, 194
Vallery-Radot, René (son-in-law), 57, 152–3, 159, 169, 174, 178, 179, 180, 181, 187, 192, 193, 194
Vaucluse department, 164
Vercel, Jules, 14, 176
Veterinary School, Alfort, 133
Veterinary School, Central, Paris, 161
Veterinary School, Turin, 161

Vienna, 42, 44, 114
Villa Vicentina, Illyria, 111, 112, 114
Villeneuve l'Etang, 169, 194, 195
vinegar, research on, 79–81, 87; *see also* fermentations
virulent diseases, 51, 68, 73, 87–91, 92–6, 122, 130–5 141, 144–52, 154–5, 189–91
virus–vaccines, 149–52, 161–2, 164–5, 168, 170–2
Vone, Théodore, 176, 177
Vulpian, Edme Félix Alfred, 177, 186

Weiss, Jean-Jacques, 98
Whitfield brewery, London, 120–1
wine, studies on, 79–84, 104, 105, 119, 120, 194, 197
Wine and Its Maladies (1866), Louis Pasteur, 83–4
Wurtz, Charles Adolphe, 142

yellow fever, 154
Yersin, Alexandre Emile John, 190

Zwickau, 41, 42

A NOTE ABOUT THE AUTHOR

Pasteur Vallery-Radot, born in Paris in 1886, is the son of the great scientist's daughter and René Vallery-Radot. Educated at the University of Paris, he has been a practicing physician since 1920, and professor of medicine at the University of Paris since 1929. In his own right one of Europe's outstanding figures in medical research, and a member of the Académie Française, he visited the United States in December 1956 to lecture at various hospitals and universities. In addition to numerous medical books and articles, Dr. Vallery-Radot is the author of two books about Pasteur: *Pasteur Inconnu* and *Images de la vie et de l'œuvre de Pasteur,* and editor of Pasteur's *Œuvres completes* and his *Correspondance.* In writing this Great Life in Brief, he has drawn extensively upon family letters and documents, as well as his own recollections of his grandfather's last years.

A NOTE ON THE TYPE

This book was set on the Linotype in a face called *Eldorado,* so named by its designer, WILLIAM ADDISON DWIGGINS, as an echo of Spanish adventures in the Western World. The series of experiments that culminated in this type-face began in 1942; the designer was trying a page more "brunette" than the usual book type. "One wanted a face that should be sturdy, and yet not too mechanical. . . . Another desideratum was that the face should be narrowish, compact, and close fitted, for reasons of economy of materials." The specimen that started Dwiggins on his way was a type design used by the Spanish printer A. de Sancha at Madrid about 1774. Eldorado, however, is in no direct way a copy of that letter, though it does reflect the Madrid specimen in the anatomy of its arches, curves, and junctions. Of special interest in the lower-case letters are the stresses of color in the blunt, sturdy serifs, subtly counterbalanced by the emphatic weight of some of the terminal curves and finials. The roman capitals are relatively open, and winged with liberal serifs and an occasional festive touch.

This book was composed by The Plimpton Press, Norwood, Massachusetts, and printed and bound by H. Wolff, New York. Paper manufactured by S. D. Warren Company, Boston. The typography and binding were designed by the creator of its type-face—W. A. Dwiggins.